Targeting Students' Science Misconceptions

Physical Science Concepts Using the Conceptual Change Model

Written by

Joseph Stepans, Ph.D.

Patent
#4,794,712
#5,293,705
#5,911,522

www.showboard.com

SHOWBOARD ®

"THE BOARD OF CHOICE" ®

Published and distributed by
Showboard, Inc.
P.O. Box 10656
Tampa, FL 33679-0656
(800) 323-9189

ISBN 1-891022-07-5

Acknowledgements

To Professor Sally Deroo of Oakland University for many valuable recommendations for this edition.

To Dr. Barbara Saigo of St. Cloud University for her valuable work in editing and her many expert and helpful suggestions.

To Paul Miller for his great contributions in editing the content and the writing.

To Robert Zekiel "Zeke" for his help with the literature search.

To science educators, authors and researchers whose work and ideas have been used in this book.

Thanks

To my family for the encouragement and support.

To many teachers, students, colleagues and graduate students across the country who have been part of the workshops, conference presentations and classes, particularly the TRIAD participants, for accepting these ideas and implementing them and for their encouragement to produce this book.

For my family

This edition is dedicated to the memory of my mother, Lucy, my brothers - Baba, Isaac, and James.

TABLE OF CONTENTS

A Foreword From the Author

We have received many comments about previous editions of this book, including valuable suggestions for additions and revisions. We are very grateful to students, teachers, administrators, and college-level faculty members who have taken the time to communicate with us. As with the previous edition, we have taken their recommendations seriously, and the following revisions have been made in this edition.

- Added a chapter on more recent physical science concepts, based on the *National Science Education Standards* for students in secondary grades and using the conceptual change strategy as the general format for activities.

- In the chapter on matter, suggested use of a long, narrow tube instead of a graduated cylinder.

- To the chapter on transformation of energy, added the topic of alternative energy sources and an activity on energy and recycling.

- To the chapter on geometry, revised area and volume activities and added new activities.

- To the pendulum chapter, added an activity to connect algebra and the behavior of a pendulum.

- To the density and buoyancy chapter, added an activity to give students the opportunity to collect and synthesize quantitative data.

- To the liquids chapter, added an activity on adhesion and cohesion.

MISCONCEPTIONS AND CONCEPTUAL CHANGE: An Introduction

HOW DOES THE MAIL GET HERE?

As children, my brothers and I would get excited when my father came home from the store announcing the arrival of a letter from abroad. Some of our relatives lived in Russia and a few others in America. When my father would say,"We got a letter today!", one of us would ask, "From whom?" Another brother would wonder, "How long did it take to get here?" My father would respond after looking at the date. Someone else would ask, "How did it come?" Again my father would look at the envelope and say by water, air, or land. The first time he responded, "By water," I took the envelope and looked at it. IT WAS DRY! I opened it, looked carefully at the writing—no indication of it being in the water!

Being the eldest of five brothers, though still young, I was usually responsible for mailing family letters. The closest mailbox was a little one that hung on the wall outside a book-store. I had envisioned that behind the mailbox there was a big hole that led to the rivers under the ground that eventually led to the big oceans. As I dropped the letter, I would put my ear to the mailbox trying to hear the letter hitting the water. Sometimes I thought I actually heard it hit the water, and I knew then it was on its way. Upon reaching the river, I imagined the letter was carried to the ocean where there were special winds at work. If the letter were to go to Russia, winds from a particular direction would carry the letter toward Russia, and if it were to go to America, there were other winds that were responsible for carrying it to its destination. I had imagined that my aunt or grandmother was waiting on the other side of the ocean for the letter, day after day. Finally, she would see it floating on the water, carried to her by the waves. She would scream with joy and run into the water to retrieve her letter. She would then stand in line to dry her letter. I had envisioned a man who had opened a letter-drying business and charged people a certain amount of money to drop their letters in a large cylinder with holes in it and dry them by turning a crank. This is how I explained to myself why the letters were not wet.

If my father told us the letter came by air, I had much more difficulty visualizing how the letters were able to survive winds from different directions and still reach their destination.

One day, when I was a young boy, I was approaching the bookstore with the little mailbox outside it, and saw a uniformed man carrying a large bag. He walked up to the mailbox, took out a set of keys, unlocked it, removed a stack of letters, and placed them in the bag. In a way I was disappointed that there was no hole behind the box, but what I saw partly explained how mail went from one place to another (Stepans, 1988).*

*From: What are we learning from children about teaching and learning? *The Journal of Natural Inquiry*, 2(2), Winter 1988. Reprinted with permission.

Every one of our students brings to the classroom his or her stories about the mail and other things in the world. This book is a small vehicle to let our students know that we acknowledge what they bring with them and to provide them with an opportunity and a place to share their views and to revise them if necessary.

THE NEED FOR AN IMPROVED APPROACH TO TEACHING AND LEARNING

When do we first formally encounter such topics as phases of the moon and the seasons? Examination of science curricula reveals that these topics first appear as early as first grade, then are repeated every two or three years in most elementary and middle level curricula. Students encounter them yet again in earth and space science, astronomy, and possibly even physics.

The videotape, "A Private Universe," produced by Pyramid Film & Video, shows interviews with 23 randomly selected Harvard graduates and faculty members and a group of ninth graders on their understanding of the causes of phases of the moon and the seasons. In one-to-one conversations, Harvard graduates and faculty members provide explanations that are practically the same and as inaccurate as those given by 9th graders. The main difference is in the terminology used, which makes the Harvard graduates and faculty members appear to have more sophisticated and "convincing" explanations than the 9th graders. Astonishingly, however, the responses given by 21 of the 23 adults show a definite lack of understanding of these *fundamental* topics.

Since 1981 I have been studying, identifying, and learning about helping students to overcome their naive ideas and misconceptions in science and mathematics. It has been educational as well as exciting to talk to students on a one-to-one basis and to collaborate with classroom teachers and higher education faculty in this endeavor. The emphasis has been on identifying, first-hand, students' views of science and mathematics concepts, then examining the success or lack of success of the way we have been teaching in helping students overcome their naive ideas. This process of replacing a naive or flawed understanding of a concept with a scientifically acceptable understanding is called conceptual change.

WHAT ARE SOME OF THE PROBLEMS WITH THE WAY WE TEACH SCIENCE?

Many bright and educated adults feel inadequate about their understanding of science phenomena. As a result, they have given up trying to make sense of even the most fundamental concepts that are taught in elementary science classrooms. Science *content* is not the only problem, however, because many adults also accepted long ago that they do not understand *science itself*. For a large number of adults, science concepts and the world described by special words, formulas, theories, and generalizations remain foreign and unapproachable. Teachers, as a group, are no exception to this sense of inadequacy and frustration. In Figure I, we could replace the words "Algebra" and "Geometry" with physics

FIGURE I.   ©1988 FORT WORTH STAR-TELEGRAM   (Reprinted with permission)

and chemistry as inhumane areas for a large number of our students and adults.

Classrooms also are distanced from the research in science education. As a result, what is taught and how it is taught are frequently and persistently contrary to the trends and suggestions educators are making about what should be happening in science education. For example, the research continues to demonstrate that each of us has our own strongly held personal theories about how things work and about science phenomena. Most of the time, these personal views do not coincide with scientific explanations, as demonstrated in the Harvard videotape. The concepts and beliefs we bring to a learning situation are the product of our first-hand experiences, common sense, what we have been told by others, media, books, and instruction.

Do schools help learners change their naive ideas and misconceptions? Do textbooks and teachers acknowledge students' personal mental models as a starting point for instruction? How meaningful are the explanations, terms, and formulas learners encounter in science classes? If they do not become meaningful as a result of instruction, why not? Science educators and concerned teachers know from formal research and from their own experiences that much of what happens in science classes involves disjointed and disconnected concepts, mystifying terminology, and irrelevant symbols, which not only do not help us make sense of our world, but may cause even more frustration and confusion.

One of the major reasons for the inconsistency between what we should do and what we actually do is the dominant role of tests and testing in our schools. Often the reason given for a particular classroom approach is that students must be "prepared" for a test, for the next grade level or course, or for high school or college. Testing is focused on benchmarks in the curriculum rather than on aiding learning. We forget about what is important, relevant, and meaningful to learners *now*, when they are grappling with complex and often confusing concepts that do not conform to their existing ideas and explanations.

Also, we have not systematically tried to examine alternative approaches to instruction which can improve, not only students' understanding of concepts and their attitudes toward learning, but also their performance on tests. A small group of learners do benefit from the traditional approach of being presented the product of scientists' work and imagination in the form of rules, laws, and generalizations. Such an approach is not helpful to the majority of students, however. It creates in them a feeling of helplessness, forces them to merely memorize the definitions, rules, laws, and formulas and makes them grateful that it will all "go away" as soon as the exams are over.

This kind of science experience is an injustice. The world and the things in it belong to all of us, its phenomena affect us all, and we are all entitled to understand it. In fact, it is increasingly important that we do understand it so we can manage our human relationships with the world appropriately. This kind of understanding is essential to all of us. It should not belong only to scientists or to the small percentage of people who happen to be able to analyze and make sense of the ways scientists, textbook writers, and other experts explain and interpret things. At the classroom level, therefore, we need to find alternative ways of making learning meaningful if the traditional approach of presenting the "adult's" view of the world does not make sense and is not helpful to young learners.

Sheila Tobias (1991) tells us that science is made more difficult by the way it is presented in textbooks and in classrooms. Textbook writers, teachers, and scientists expect learners to immediately accept what they are given and make sense of it later. The Calvin and Hobbs cartoon (Figure II) is as true for science as it is for mathematics. As it indicates, for many students the presentation of abstract concepts makes them mysterious beyond comprehension — easier to accept as "magic" than to learn. Science is made difficult to understand because books and teachers usually begin with definitions, symbols, and abstractions, before the students have had the opportunity to understand the concept or relate it meaningfully to what they already know and believe.

Calvin and Hobbes   by Bill Watterson

Figure II.   CALVIN AND HOBBES copyright 1991 Watterson. Reprinted with permission of UNIVERSAL PRESS SYNDICATE. All rights reserved.

Even though each of us encounters scientific phenomena as concrete experiences, much of science — particularly in the physical sciences — hides behind mathematical abstractions. For instance, in a graduate course in quantum mechanics, twice a week our professor would walk into class, pick up a piece of chalk, and write equations going from one side of the board to another for the next 75 minutes without turning his face to us. We were so busy copying the formulas that we never had the opportunity to ask questions or clarify what the symbols represented. Our immediate concern was to copy the information we needed for the next exam rather than to understand what we were copying.

Learning, especially when it involves abstract concepts, is a complex process. For most of us it takes time to really learn something. It requires activity, discussion, and establishing relationships among various components. In order for learning to occur, the gap between the learner (where the learner is, what the learner is capable of understanding) and the concept presented should be manageable for the learner to bridge with the instructional experiences that are provided. We should attempt to change the image presented in the cartoon for our students.

We often hear teachers express frustration that they feel obligated to "cover" everything in the curriculum or in the textbook. At a time when scientific knowledge is increasing exponentially, however, teachers need to make *decisions* about what is important to do in their classes. Do they want to cover more factual information? Do they want to emphasize problem solving and decision-making skills? Do they want their students to develop positive attitudes toward science and toward learning in general? Do they want their students to make connections between what happens in class and the out-of-class world? Will they be satisfied with having students perform low-order recall tasks or do they want their students to develop conceptual change?

As educators, we presently have a wonderful opportunity to implement effective, learner-based teaching strategies that grow from the research on how learning occurs. We need to rethink what we teach, how we teach, and how we assess what happens to the learner. We should put our emphasis on creating meaningful changes in learners and help them to look at the world differently — more knowledgeably and confidently. And more importantly, we should create an atmosphere in which the learner is motivated *to want to learn more*.

According to the research, this kind of learning can occur when we provide experiences that acknowledge and directly challenge students' naive conceptions. In these experiences, students encounter situations in which the events and explanations are not immediately obvious and are somewhat contrary to their innate feelings or experiences. Because these situations may not quite make sense, they have the potential of creating in the learner a conflict between what she or he expects to happen and what actually happens. It is the desire or need to resolve this conflict which creates in the learner a motivation to learn. Out of this conflict, conceptual change can emerge.

We need to recognize that learning is a complex process, that it takes time to learn, that our students are different from one another, and that they learn differently. The learning environment should be rich and varied enough to encompass the different learning styles that students bring to our classes.

CHANGING STUDENTS' NAIVE IDEAS THROUGH A CONCEPTUAL CHANGE STRATEGY

Posner, Strike, Hewson, & Gertzog (1982) and Strike and Posner (1985) tell us that in order to bring about a conceptual change in students with respect to a concept, several conditions are necessary:

- the students must be dissatisfied with their existing views.
- the new conception must appear somewhat plausible.
- the new conception must be more attractive.
- the new conception must have explanatory and predictive power.

The **conceptual change strategy** used in this book as the method of presenting science concepts to students attempts to address the above conditions. This strategy helps students to become *aware* of their private views and to *confront* them. The approach *actively engages* students, who learn by anticipation and prediction of outcomes, by verbalizing and sharing their own ideas, by listening to each other, by actually testing their predictions and explanations, and by verbalizing what they have learned. It helps students learn by constantly revising their mental models about how things work and by connecting what goes on in class to other aspects of their lives. It encourages them to continue to think about the issues discussed outside the class and to look for other examples and applications of the new concept.

The development of the teaching for conceptual change model (CCM) is the result of work by many science educators, teachers, and other professionals and friends of education. Some of those who have contributed to developing and implementing the conceptual change model are listed below, along with some publication references: Eaton, Anderson, & Smith (1983), Clement (1987), Nussbaum & Novick (1981) , Posner, Strike, Hewson, & Gertzog (1982) , Driver & Scanlon (1989), Duit (1987), Feher & Rice (1985), Gilbert, Osborne, & Fensham (1982), and Stepans (1988, 1991).

The traditional *learning cycle*, developed by Atkins & Karplus in the 1960's (Atkins & Karplus,1962) and implemented in SCIS (Science Curriculum Improvement Study) and other science curricula, has made great contributions to activity-oriented science programs. The classical learning cycle consists of three phases: exploration, concept invention, and application. It utilizes ideas put forth by such noted psychologists as Jean Piaget (1965) and Jerome Bruner (1960) . The learning cycle opened the door for developing a fuller, more effective strategy or model for instruction based on continuing research on the learning process. The conceptual change strategy, as described on the next page, does not dismiss the learning cycle. It acknowledges its value but, as illustrated, goes beyond the learning cycle in some meaningful ways.

The **Conceptual Change Model (CCM)** places students in an environment that encourages them to confront their own preconceptions and those of their classmates, then work toward resolution and conceptual change. The model consists of six stages:

1. Students *become aware* of their own preconceptions about a concept by thinking about it and making predictions (*committing to an outcome*) before any activity begins.

2. Students *expose their beliefs* by sharing them, initially in small groups and then with the entire class.

3. Students *confront their beliefs* by testing and discussing them in small groups.

4. Students work toward *resolving conflicts* (if any) between their ideas (based on the revealed preconceptions and class discussion) and their observations, thereby *accommodating the new concept*.

5. Students *extend the concept* by trying to *make connections* between the concept learned in the classroom and other situations, including their daily lives.

6. Students are encouraged to *go beyond*, pursuing additional questions and problems of their choice related to the concept.

ABOUT THIS BOOK

The purpose of this book is to share with teachers and other educators the *use of the conceptual change strategy as applied to physical science topics* which are difficult for students to understand. Most of the activities use the conceptual change model. They have been successfully tested with learners at all levels and have been shown to be effective in several ways. They promote student enthusiasm for learning. They provide opportunities for students to share and learn from each other, and encourage participation by students with a variety of learning styles. They provide immediate opportunities for students to process the learning experience. In many instances, they have brought about meaningful changes in students' naive ideas as well as increasing their motivation for further learning.

I am not claiming that the students who are exposed to the teaching for conceptual change model will immediately abandon their naive preconceptions and misconceptions in favor of the scientists' explanations of the concept. Preexisting beliefs are tenacious and may require repeated challenges in different settings and contexts to replace. I do believe, however, that teaching for conceptual change provides an exciting and effective learning alternative for children. Many teachers who have used the model support this belief.

FORMAT FOR THE TOPICS IN THIS BOOK

Each Topic (unless otherwise indicated) will follow a consistent format, including:

A.   Identification of the Concept (a single concept or a set of related concepts)
B.   Background Information for the Teacher
C.   Some Representative Student Misconceptions Related to the Concept
D.   Sources of Students' Confusion and Misconceptions
E.   Learning about the Topic Using the Conceptual Change Model
      (Teaching Notes and Activities)
F.   References

In the activities, "shorthand" designations have been provided for the six steps of the CCM. (Some of the terms were first used by Feher and Rice, 1986.) Also, the stages are consistently numbered, 1-6, in the activities. The numbers and short identifiers are:

  1. *commit to an outcome*
  2. *expose beliefs*
  3. *confront beliefs*
  4. *accommodate the concept*
  5. *extend the concept*
  6. *go beyond*

Section E includes Teaching Notes and Activities. The teaching notes include a list of equipment and materials needed for the student activities, safety tips, any advance preparation, and other helpful notes for teachers. The Activities pages may be reproduced for students whenever appropriate. Teachers may choose to use these pages as a teaching guide, rather than as student reproducibles, when working with very young learners.

TEACHERS: SOME NOTES ABOUT USING THE CCM

Teachers can use a variety of approaches for each step of the conceptual change strategy. Here are some suggestions:

Step 1. To help students become aware of their own beliefs with respect to a concept, the teacher may pose a question, present a challenge, or call on students to make predictions about the outcome. What the teacher is doing is encouraging the student to COMMIT TO AN OUTCOME.

Step 2. The teacher may ask students to share their ideas initially in small groups, then with the entire class to expose their beliefs and become aware of the beliefs of others about the concept. Beginning the sharing in a small group initially provides many students a secure environmnent before they tell everyone in class what they think. Moving from small to whole group gives the student the opportunity to EXPOSE HIS/HER BELIEFS. It also gives the student an opportunity to see that others are also uncertain and bring a variety of views to the situations. In the case of primary students, it may be sufficient to have them share their views in their small groups of 3 or 4. Experience has shown that young students may not pay attention when one student presents to the large group.

Step 3. Students can test their ideas by manipulating materials. Students also may at times confront and debate their ideas, conduct interviews, and check written materials. This is an opportunity for students to CONFRONT BELIEFS.

Step 4. In helping students (especially young learners) to develop a **conceptual change** or **begin to process** the targeted concepts, the teacher may pose questions, drawing on students' observations and discussions to help them process information or begin to make sense of the "why" behind the observations. This is the phase where the student begins to resolve *the conflict* that may exist between his/her beliefs and what is observed. Doing this, the student will ACCOMMODATE THE CONCEPT.

Step 5. To help students to apply the concept to other situations, including their daily lives, the teacher may ask students to give examples of where they have seen the concept discussed or demonstrated, or may bring their own examples on how the concept is connected to other situations. This provides students with the opportunity to EXTEND THE CONCEPT.

Step 6. The last step encourages the students to continue thinking about the concept and pursue additional questions and problems of interest to them. This stage is important because it serves to establish in the students' minds that just because the concept has been discussed in class and connections are made, it does not mean learning is over. In doing this, students will GO BEYOND.

ASSESSMENT

Assessment should be an important component of the learning process. It should be matched to our expectations of the student and to the way we teach. If we value understanding, if we value thinking and decision-making skills, if we value enthusiasm and a positive attitude toward science for our students, then we have to plan to assess them appropriately. Just as the teaching for conceptual change model provides appropriate *experiences* for students to achieve what is expected, appropriate *assessment* strategies are also vital to insure that what we had hoped to happen to the student did, in fact, happen. Since, we are concentrating on all domains–knowing, applying, developing appropriate skills, developing positive feelings toward science, the learning of science, and habits of mind–our assessment should be geared to addressing all these domians.

The key is to align (1) our expectations of students, (2) the experiences we provide for them, and (3) our assessment. Depending on our specific expectations (objectives) for a concept, topic, or activity, we should use one of more appropriate strategies to document achievement, including interviews, performance evaulations, student writing, protfolios, observations, and student self-assessment.

AN EXAMPLE OF APPROPRIATE ASSESSMENT

We will use the topic of pendulums to illustrate an example of appropriate assessment strategies. Let us begin by clarifying our expectations of students as we go through the topic. What is it that we hope to accomplish? Some examples of appropriate expectations are listed below. Feel free to add to the list or otherwise adapt it to your own student expectations.

Expectations

1. Students will become aware of their beliefs related to the behavior of the pendulum.

2. Students will become aware of the views of others.

3. Students will be willing to confront their ideas.

4. Students will be willing to revise their ideas.

5. Students will extend the concept of the pendulum as demonstrated in classroom activities to other situations and applications.

6. Students will go beyond with their knowledge of the pendulum outside of class, continuing to test their understanding.

7. Students will collaborate with others.

8. Students will show respect for the opinions of others.

9. Students will collect necessary data.

10. Students will identify and control appropriate variables.

11. Students will establish relationships among variables.

12. Students will initiate ideas.

13. Students will show persistence.

14. Students will communicate data and analysis of data using various modes (speaking, writing, tables, graphs, drawings).

15. Students will exhibit confidence in pursuing questions about the pendulum.

16. Students will appreciate the importance of the study of the pendulum.

17. Students will enjoy being challenged.

18. Students will develop a conceptual understanding of the pendulum.

ASSESSMENT STRATEGIES

Again it must be stressed that assessment should be an important part of learning. It should be <u>tied closely</u> to (1) *our expectations of students* and (2) *the experiences we provide for them*. From the list of expectations , it is clear that we need a <u>variety</u> of ways to assess whether the expectations are met.

To gain insight into students' conceptual understanding, skills, attitudes, and behaviors, we need to use various strategies to collect necessary information. Some of the strategies may include *interviewing, observation, performance, projects, and pencil and paper tools*. <u>In addition</u> to teacher assessment, we should provide the <u>students</u> with the opportunity to reflect on the evolution of their own ideas, changes in their skill levels, attitudes, and behaviors.

Some examples of assessment strategies are displayed in the tables on pages 12–14. The tables <u>align expectations with assessment</u> by providing sample situations given to the students, assessment strategies which may be used, expectations targeted, and sample evidence showing whether the expectation is met, developing, or not met.

Situation Presented	Assessment Strategy Used	Expectation Targeted	Expectations Met	Expectations Developing	Expectations Not Met
*Suppose that you have two pendulums, equal in size, and one has wooden bob while the other one has a metal bob. Predict what would happen if you pulled both of them toward you and released them at the same time. Provide reasons for your predictions.	*Observations *Interview (individual or group) *Performance	#1	*willing to make prediction *able to predict *willing to write down reason *able to come up with sound explanation	*attempts to predict *makes effort at reasoning *attempts explanation	*resists making prediction *makes no predictions *resists writing reason *unable to explain
*Share your predictions and explanations with others in your group and then with the class	*Observation *Performance	#2	*willing to share *able to explain *able to draw on experience	*makes attempt *tries to explain	*resists sharing *unable to explain *unable to draw on experience
*Test your ideas and make revisions if necessary	*Observation *Performance	#s 4,7,8,9	*willing to test *able to set up tests *makes accurate observations *collaborates with others *incorporates others' ideas *willing to revise ideas *shows persistence	*makes an attempt	*resists testing *unable to set up tests *unable to make accurate observations *does not collaborate *unwilling to revise ideas, *gives up easily
*Make a statement explaining your understanding of the behavior of the pendulums	*Obsevations *Pencil and paper *Performance	#4	*willing to write down ideas *able to synthesize information	*makes an attempt	*not willing to write down ideas *not able to synthesize information

12

Table 1

Situation Presented	Assessment Strategy Used	Expectations Targeted	Expectations Met	Expectations Developing	Expectations Not Met
*Suppose you have two pendulums, one with a wooden ball for a bob and the other with a wooden cylinder. They are hanging from strings of equal length. Predict what would happen if you pulled them toward you and released them at the same time, comparing the time for 3-4 swings. Give explanations for your predictions	*Interview *Performance *Pencil and paper *Observation	#s 1, 2, 3, 4, 7, 8	*collaborates with others *shows respect for others' opinions	*attempts to collaborate *attempts to listen to opinions of others	*resists collaboration *shows lack of respect for others' opinions
*Given a wooden ball and a wooden cylinder hanging from strings such that the total lengths are equal, make predictions about the time taken for 3-5 swings. Give reasons for your predictions.		# 14	*willing to synthesize data from previous situation *willing to communicate concisely the behavior of the pendulum	*makes an attempt	*unwilling to synthesize previous data *unwilling to communicate behavior of pendulum

Table 2

Situation Presented	Assessment Strategy Used	Expectations Targeted	Expectations Met	Expectations Developing	Expectations Not Met
*Using situations 1-4, make a statement about what factors affect the period of a pendulum.	*Pencil and paper *Observation *Interview	#s 11,14	*is able to establish relationships among variables *is willing to communicate data and analysis of data using tables, graphs	*attempts to establish relationships *makes an attempt to communicate data	*unable to establish relationships *resists communication and analysis
*How would you extend the topic of pendulums to other situations?	*Interview *Pencil and paper	#s 12, 13, 15	*initiates ideas *shows persistence *shows confidence	*attempts to initiate ideas *shows effort	*does not initiate ideas *gives up easily *lacks confidence
*Why do we study the pendulum?	*Interview *Pencil and paper	# 16	*volunteers to bring ideas about pendulums from home	*thinks about pendulum out of class *does not attempt to bring ideas to class	
*What questions, problems, or projects would you like to pursue about pendulums?	*Interview *Pencil and paper *Observation *Project	#s 17, 18	*brings ideas for extension *exhibits a conceptual understanding	*shows interest in extending ideas *show some understanding	*does not show interest *does not show understanding
*Set up a plan to pursue your question, problem, or project. Present the results to the class.	*Performance *Observation *Project	#s 5, 6	*is able to set up appropriate situations *shows interest *enjoys challenges	*makes attempt to set up situations *indifferent to challenges	*is not interested *resists challenges

Table 3

Students may also create a *portfolio,* which includes the following statements.

- Today's (this week's) lesson was about...

- My initial thoughts and feelings about the lesson were...

- This is what we did in our small groups...

- My feelings about sharing my thoughts with others in the group were...

- The most difficult thing for me to do during the lesson was...

- My feelings during the activity were...

- I changed my thinking with respect to...

- I changed because...

- This is how I understand the behavior of a pendulum...

- I want to further investigate these questions or problems, or do a project about...

- This is how I feel about the value of studying the pendulum...

- Attached is a collection of my thoughts and work that I want to share.

- Further reactions...

REFERENCES

Atkins, M., & Karplus, R. (September, 1962). Discovery or invention? *The Science Teacher*, *29*, 45-51.

Blosser, P. (1989). Disseminating research about science education. In Motz, L, & Madrazo, G. (Eds.), *NSSA Third Sourcebook for Science Supervisors*. Washington, DC: National Science Teachers Association.

Clement, J. (1987). Overcoming student's misconceptions in physics: the role of anchoring intuitions and analogical validity. In J. Novak (Ed.), *Proceedings of the Second International Seminar on Misconceptions and Educational Strategies in Science and Mathematics (Vol. 3)*. Ithaca, NY: Cornell University, pp. 84-97.

Cronin-Jones, L. (1991). Science teacher beliefs and their influence on curriculum implementation: Two case studies. *Journal of Research in Science Teaching*, *28*, 3, pp. 235-250.

Driver, R. & Scanlon, E. (1989). Conceptual change in science. *Journal of Computer Assisted Learning*, *5*, 25-36.

Duit, R. (1987). Research on students' alternative frameworks in science — topics, theoretical frameworks, consequences for science teaching. In J. Novak (Ed.), *Proceedings of the Second International Seminar on Misconceptions and Educational Strategies in Science and Mathematics (Vol. 1)*. Ithaca, NY: Cornell University, pp. 151-162.

Eaton, J. F., Anderson, C.W., & Smith, E. L. (1983). When students don't know they don't know. *Science and Children*, *20* (7), 7-9.

Feher, E. & Rice, R. (1985). Development of scientific concepts through the use of interactive exhibits in a museum. *American Museum of Natural History*, *28*, 35-46.

Feher, E. & Rice, R. (1986). Shadow shapes. *Science and Children*, *24*(2), 6-9.

Gilbert, J., Osborne,R., & Fensham, P. (1982). Children's science and its consequences for teaching. *Science Education*, *66*, 623-633.

Kyle, W., & J. Shymansky. (Nov-Dec, 1988). What research says... about teachers as researchers. *Science and Children*, *26*, 29-31.

Maeroff, G. (1988). *The empowerment of teachers: overcoming the crisis of confidence*. New York: Teachers College Press.

Nussbaum, J., & Novick, S. (1981). Creating cognitive dissonance between students' preconceptions to encourage individual cognitive accommodation and a group cooperative construction of a scientific model. Paper presented at the AERA Annual Convention, Los Angeles, CA.

Osborne, R., & Freyberg, P. (1985). *Learning in science: The implications of children's science*. London: Heinemann.

Porter, A., & Brophy, J. (May, 1988). Synthesis of research on good teaching: insights from the work of the Institute for Research on Teaching. *Educational Leadership*.

Posner, G., Strike, K., Hewson, P., and Gertzog, W. (1982). Accommodation of a scientific conception: Toward a theory of conceptual change. *Science Education, 66*, 211-227.

Stepans, J. (1988). What are we learning from children about teaching and learning? *Journal of Natural Inquiry, 2* (2), 9-18.

Stepans, J. (1989). A partnership for making research work in the classroom. *Researcher, 6*, 1, pp. 3-5. Northern Rocky Mountain Educational Research Association.

Stepans, J. (1990). On the feasibility of research collaboration between higher education faculty and public school teachers. *Researcher, 6*, 2, pp 3-5. Northern Rocky Mountain Educational Research Association.

Stepans, J. (1991). Developmental patterns in students' understanding of physics concepts. In S. Glynn, R. Yeany, & B. Britton, (Eds.), *The psychology of learning science*. Hillsdale, NJ: Lawrence Erlbaum, Publishers.

Stepans, J., Miller, K., & Willis, C. (1992). Teacher, administrator, and university educators form a triad. *Journal of Rural and Small Schools*. Spring. (5), 2, pp. 38-41.

Strike, K., & Posner, G. (1985). A conceptual change view of learning and understanding. In L. West & A. Pines (Eds.), *Cognitive structure and conceptual change*. Orlando, FL: Academic Press.

Tobias, S. (1990). *They're not dumb, they're different: stalking the second tier*. Tucson, AZ: Research Corporation.

Tobin, K. (1990). Research on science laboratory activities: In pursuit of better questions and answers to improve learning. *School Science and Mathematics*, 90 (5), pp. 403-412.

MATTER

A.   IDENTIFICATION OF THE CONCEPTS

physical and chemical properties of matter; states of matter; acids, bases, and neutral substances

B.   BACKGROUND FOR THE TEACHER

What is the difference between acids, bases and neutral substances?

In nature, compounds fall into three categories: neutral, acidic, or basic. Lemon juice and vinegar are examples of *acids*. They are sour tasting, react with bases, and have a pH of less than 7. Because tasting is not a good way to tell if something is an acid, we use litmus paper. If a substance is an acid, it will turn blue litmus paper red.

Bases, sometimes called alkaline substances, are bitter. Ammonia and baking soda are examples of bases. They react with acids, have a pH of more than 7 and turn the red litmus paper blue.

Distilled water is an example of a *neutral* substance.   If the proper amounts of acid and base are mixed, a neutral solution can be produced. An example of this is the combination of the proper amounts of an acid called hydrochloric acid and a base called sodium hydroxide. When they come in contact, they react and produce a neutral substance, salt water.

What are "states of matter"?

Matter is categorized into states such as *solid, liquid, and gas*. We will start with the solid state. Ice is an example of the solid state of water (H_2O). Ice has a definite shape and volume, and its molecules are tightly packed and possess strong cohesive forces.

When ice melts, the substance is still the same (the chemical composition has not changed) but the *physical state* has changed. When ice melts, it becomes liquid water. Liquids have a definite volume but take the shape of the container they occupy. The molecules of water are not as tightly packed and the cohesive forces between molecules are weaker.

If we boil water (or let it evaporate), it becomes water vapor, a gaseous state. We usually call water vapor "steam," if it is the result of water being heated. Cohesive forces between gas molecules are extremely weak. The molecules are far apart, and they have no definite shape or volume.

What are physical and chemical changes?

Breaking a piece of wood, melting ice, and dissolving sugar in water are *physical* changes. After these processes, the chemical composition of the substance is the same as before the change occurred. When a piece of wood burns, when an egg is fried, or when a nail rusts, however, there is a chemical change. The substance has a different chemical composition after the change.

How do we view matter at the molecular level?

Materials that have different chemical properties are made of different *elements* or *molecules*. A molecule is the tiniest piece of a particular substance. For example, ordinary salt (sodium chloride) dissolved in water may look like plain water, but it is made up of two kinds of molecules: $NaCl$ and H_2O. By contrast, plain water is made up of only H_2O molecules, no matter if it is solid (ice), liquid (water), or gas (water vapor). It takes uncountably large numbers of molecules to make a sample of a substance visible.

The molecules of different substances have different sizes. Just as the empty spaces between marbles in a graduated cylinder can be filled with sand without increasing the total volume of the system, the spaces between the molecules of substances with large molecules like water can be filled with the smaller molecules of substances like alcohol.

What are some other properties of matter?

Materials are different in many ways. We can distinguish one material from another by its density, heat conductivity, solubility, melting point, and electrical conductivity, among other traits.

What gases make up the air?

Gas is one of the states of matter. An effective way of talking about gases is to relate them to air. Air is made up of many distinct gases. It is about 78% nitrogen, 21% oxygen, 0.94% argon, and 0.04% carbon dioxide. Many of these gases react with other substances. To give some examples, oxygen makes a burning splint glow (flare), hydrogen makes it pop (explode), and carbon dioxide makes the flame go out. Another visible example is when blowing carbon dioxide into lime water makes the lime water turn milky because of a chemical reaction with the gas.

Oxygen is the most chemically active gas in the air. It oxidizes—combines with— many elements at room temperature. An example of this is the rusting of iron. The rate of this process is increased in the presence of moisture. When, for example, steel wool is placed in a test tube, then inverted with the open end submerged in water, the formation of rust removes gaseous oxygen from the tube. As a result, the gas pressure is reduced and the outside atmospheric pressure pushes water up into the tube.

Carbon dioxide is present in a variety of carbonate minerals and rocks. For example, it is quite abundant in limestone. Carbon dioxide in the atmosphere is the ultimate carbon source for organic molecules—carbohydrates, fats, proteins, and nucleic acids--of which all living things are made. During the process of photosynthesis, organisms that contain the green pigment, chlorophyll, incorporate carbon dioxide into sugar molecules, the basic source of energy and carbon molecules for cells. Pure oxygen is returned to the atmosphere as a byproduct of photosynthesis. In the laboratory, carbon dioxide may be produced by combining any acid (such as vinegar) and a carbonated compound (such as baking soda). Visible carbon dioxide bubbles are also produced when Alka Seltzer is put in water.

C.   SOME REPRESENTATIVE STUDENT MISCONCEPTIONS ABOUT MATTER

♦   Gases are not matter because they are invisible.

♦   Air and oxygen are the same thing.

♦   Particles of matter possess properties that we associate with macroscopic matter. For example, gold atoms are shiny and hard, or water molecules are tiny droplets.

♦   Expansion of matter is due to the expansion of the particles, rather than the increase of particle spacing.

♦   Mass and volume both vaguely describe the "amount of matter."

♦   Chemical changes are perceived as additive, rather than interactive. After chemical change, the original substances are perceived as remaining, even though they are altered.

♦   Failure to perceive that individual substances and properties correspond to a certain type of particle leads to the impression that formation of a substance simply happens. The fact that particles actually are rearranged is often missed.

D.   SOURCES OF STUDENTS' CONFUSION AND MISCONCEPTIONS

♦   Scientific models used to teach the concepts of matter are abstract.

♦   There often is unexplored conflict between students' everyday experiences and the classroom or textbook presentation.

♦   Students' notions about physical and chemical behavior of matter interact with the presentations in textbooks and by teachers, resulting in confusion and misconceptions.

♦   Some of the language used by teachers and textbooks may confuse some students.

♦   If we use a model for an atom, the properties of that model are often inappropriately assigned to the atom.

♦   Many students, even those at the college level, extend macroscopic properties like color and hardness to the atomic/molecular level.

♦   Students' views about matter do not evolve as quickly as the rate of concept presentation in most classrooms and most textbooks.

♦   Instructional materials used to convey abstract concepts are often two-dimensional diagrams with symbols.

♦   Models made of common objects, such as toothpicks, marshmallows, Styrofoam balls, or nuts and bolts may lead students to literally transfer the attributes of the models to what they are supposed to represent.

♦   Many students lack the formal level of thinking and spatial skills to make sense of textbook presentations, instructional models, and demonstrations about matter and the behavior of matter.

E.   LEARNING ABOUT MATTER USING THE CONCEPTUAL CHANGE MODEL

TEACHING NOTES

Provide the following materials for each small group:

rubbing alcohol (Ethanol)	flashlight battery (6 volt)
water	bulb
salt	wire
sugar	lemon juice
vinegar	Alka Seltzer tablet
cornstarch	7-Up
baking soda	Pepsi
plaster of Paris	vegetable oil
wax paper	dish detergent
droppers	ice cube tray
wooden matches	citric acid crystals
steel wool	test tubes
balance scale	glass tube or eudiometer (80-100 cm long)

rubber stopper (with tubing) to fit test tube
5 solids (same 5 for all groups)
red cabbage juice indicator
food coloring

To make red cabbage juice indicator: heat red cabbage in distilled water until water turns purple. Discard cabbage. (Juice can be frozen in ice cube trays ahead of time for easy storage. Just thaw out a cube for each group for acid/base activity.)

How to produce an oxide for heating in activity VII: Place 5 grams of citric acid crystals and about 4 grams steel wool in a test tube. Add 25 ml of vinegar. Insert a rubber stopper (with a piece of rubber tubing in it) into the test tube. Place the other end of the tubing in the mouth of a second test tube that is filled with water and held upside down in a container of water. As it forms, the hydrogen will fill the second test tube, displacing the water. Enough hydrogen will be collected for testing in about 45-60 minutes. Hold the burning match over the mouth of the gas-filled test tube.

Caution: Students should wear safety glasses while working with the burning match and gases. Students should wet the ends of matches before discarding them.

ACTIVITY I: How Much Matter?

A. <u>Adding alcohol and water</u>

1. Commit to an outcome

You have a narrow, approximately one-meter long glass tube. Fill it halfway with colored water. I you gently pour ethanol until it is completely filled:

a. What will happen to the liquids? Give reasons for your prediction.

b. Next, what do you predict will happen inside the tube if you place a stopper in the open end, making certain there are no air bubbles present, and inverting the tube several times? Give re sons for your prediction.

2. Expose Beliefs

Share your beliefs about how much liquid will result and your explanations with the other members of your group. Choose someone from your group to share with the class the predictions and the explanations of each member of the group.

3. Confront Beliefs

Get graduated cylinders, water, and alcohol, and test your predictions. After making your observations, make any appropriate changes in your explanations.

B. <u>Salt in water and sugar in water</u>

1. Commit to an Outcome

Suppose you have two graduated cylinders; one is filled halfway with regular salt and the other is filled halfway with sugar. If you added water to both cylinders until they were full, then let the cylinders sit for awhile, what do you predict will happen to the water level? Predict what will happen to the level of the salt and the sugar. Explain the reasons behind your prediction.

2. Expose Beliefs

Share with others in your group your predictions and explanations about what will happen to the water levels with salt and with sugar.

3. Confront Beliefs

Get the graduated cylinders, salt, sugar, and water, and test your predictions. What really happens when you add water to the half-full cylinders and wait for a time?

4. Accommodate the Concept

Based on your observations in Activities A and B above, what statement can you make about this behavior of matter? How are A and B similar and how are they different? Share your statements with others in your group.

5. Extend the Concept

What are some examples related to the phenomena in A and B with which you are familiar?

6. Go Beyond

What questions, problems, and projects related to the concept you would like to pursue? Share any ideas with the class.

ACTIVITY II: Powders and Vinegar

1. Commit to an Outcome

Predict what will happen if you add a few drops of vinegar to each of the following powders: salt, corn starch, baking soda, and plaster of Paris. Explain the reasons for your predictions.

2. Expose Beliefs

Share with others in your group your predictions and explanations about the effect of vinegar on the powders.

3. Confront Beliefs

Get the powders, vinegar, waxed paper and droppers, test your predictions and revise your explanations, if necessary.

4. Accommodate the Concept

Based on your observations and discussions, what statements can you make about the effect of vinegar on different powders?

5. Extend the Concept

Can you think of examples and applications of this phenomenon? Share these ideas with others in your group.

6. Go Beyond

What related questions, problems, and projects would you like to pursue?

ACTIVITY III: Do All Liquids Freeze?

1. Commit to an Outcome

If you prepared an ice tray containing water, salt water, rubbing alcohol, vegetable oil, and vinegar in separate compartments and placed it in the freezer overnight, what will happen to each material? (Record the temperature of the freezer).

2. Expose Beliefs

Share with others in your group your predictions and explanations as to what would happen to the liquids placed in the freezer. Select someone from your group to present to the class the predictions and explanations of each member of the group.

3. Confront Beliefs

Prepare an ice tray containing tap water, salt water, vinegar, vegetable oil, and rubbing alcohol and place it overnight in the freezer. The next day, remove the tray and test your predictions. Are there changes you want to make in your explanations?

4. Accommodate the Concept

What statement can you make based on what you have observed and on your discussion as to what caused some liquids to freeze while others did not. Can all liquids be frozen at the temperature of the freezer you recorded? Share your statement with others in your group.

5. Extend the Concept

Where have you seen examples of this phenomenon? What are some of the applications of this phenomenon? Share these ideas with others in your group.

6. Go Beyond

What additional questions, problems, and projects do you want to pursue on the freezing of liquids?

ACTIVITY IV: Which Liquids Conduct Electricity?

1. Commit to an Outcome

Predict if any of these liquids will conduct electricity: water, strong salt solution, liquid detergent, baking soda solution, and vinegar. Explain why you think so.

2. Expose Beliefs

Share with others in your group your predictions and explanations about which liquids will conduct electricity. Again, choose a representative from your group to share the predictions and explanations of the members with the rest of your class.

3. Confront Beliefs

Get the liquids, a battery, wires, and light bulb. As a group, test your ideas (see Figure 2) and discuss the changes you may want to make in your explanations.

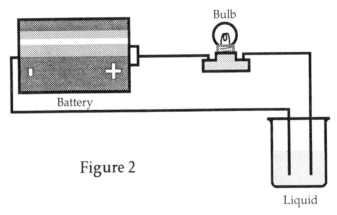

Figure 2

4. Accommodate the Concept

Based on your observations and group discussions, what statement can you make about the type of liquid that will conduct electricity? How would you account for this property of matter?

5. Extend the Concept

What are some of the applications of this phenomenon? Can you think of examples of liquids conducting electricity?

6. Go Beyond

What additional questions, problems, or projects about a liquid's ability to conduct electricity would you like to pursue?

ACTIVITY V: Acids, Bases, and Neutral Compounds

1. Commit to an Outcome

Predict what will happen to the color of red cabbage juice if we add: lemon juice, Alka Seltzer solution, Pepsi, water, baking soda solution, soap water, and 7-up. Explain why you think so.

2. Expose Beliefs

Share with others in your group your predictions and explanations about what will happen to the color of red cabbage juice when each substance is added.

3. Confront Beliefs

Get the cabbage juice, water, lemon juice, Alka Seltzer solution, Pepsi, soap water, baking soda solution, and 7-up, and test your predictions. Do your observations agree with your predictions? Discuss your thinking with others in your group.

4. Accommodate the Concept

Based on your observations, how would you classify the the liquids? What statement can you make about the liquids in each group? Are there some other ways in which the liquids in each group are similar?

5. Extend the Concept

What are some other examples of substances like these? What are some of the applications of these properties of liquids?

6. Go Beyond

What additional questions, problems, and projects would you like to pursue related to this concept?

ACTIVITY VI: Describing A Solid

1. Commit to an Outcome

Can you describe a solid fully so that others can identify it? Explain what characteristics you would use to describe a solid.

2. Expose Beliefs

Share with others in your group your ideas about the characteristics one needs to use to fully describe a solid. Have someone from your group present your ideas and those of others in your group to the large group.

3. Confront Beliefs

Every group will be given the same five solids. Using all the characteristics you mentioned and, working as a group, choose one of the solids and describe it. Challenge the other groups to select from the five the solid you had chosen based on your description.

4. Accommodate the Concept

Based on your results and the discussion, what characteristics are needed to fully describe a substance? With others in the group, develop the notion of texture, density, heat conductivity, electrical conductivity, and other properties of matter.

5. Extend the Concept

Share with others how such properties of matter help us in our lives.

6. Go Beyond

What other questions, problems, and projects would you like to undertake related to properties of matter?

ACTIVITY VII: Predict What Gas Is Produced

1. Commit to an Outcome

Predict what will happen to the flame exposed to gas produced by (a) Alka Seltzer added to water and (b) heating an oxide. Explain your reasons for your predictions.

2. Expose Beliefs

Share with others in your group your predictions and explanations about what you think will happen if a lighted match is brought close to the two gases produced above. Choose a representative from your group to present the predictions and explanations of the members to the class.

3. Confront Beliefs

Get the necessary materials and, under direction from your teacher, test your predictions. **Be very careful with the lighted match.** What changes, if any, do you want to make in your explanations?

4. Accommodate the Concept

Based on your observations and discussions, what statements can you make about the properties of the gases produced? What other properties do the two gases have? Check with your teacher for other ideas.

5. Extend the Concept

What are some of the examples of these gases with which you are familiar? What are the applications of this idea?

6. Go Beyond

What are some additional questions, problems, or projects you would like to pursue about gases and their properties?

Balloons and gases. (1971). Elementary Science Study (ESS) Series. St. Louis: McGraw-Hill.

Bar, V. & Travis, A.S. (1991). Children's views concerning phase changes. *Journal of Research in Science Teaching, 28,(4)*, 363-382.

Driver, R. (1985). Beyond appearances: the conservation of matter under physical and chemical transformations. In Driver, R.,Guesne, E., and Tiberghien, A.(Eds.), *Children's ideas in science*. Philadelphia: Open University Press.

Friedel, A. (1991). *Teaching science to children*. New York: McGraw-Hill.

Gabel, D.L., Samuel, K. V., & Hunn, D. (August 1987). Understanding the particulate nature of matter. *Journal of Chemical Education, 64 (8)*, 695-697.

Gases and "Airs". (1967). Elementary Science Study (ESS) Series. St. Louis: McGraw-Hill.

Griffiths, A. K. & Preston, K. R. (1992). Grade-12 students' misconceptions relating to fundamental characteristics of atoms and molecules. *Journal of Research in Science Teaching, 29 (6)*, 611-628.

Hapkiewicz, A. & Hapkiewicz, W. G. (1993). *Misconceptions in science*. Presented at the National Science Teachers Association Regional Meeting, Denver.

Liem, T. (1987). *Invitations to science inquiry*. Lexington,MA: Ginn Press.

Mas, C., Perez, J., & Harris, H. H. (July 1987). Parallels between adolescents' conception of gases and the history of chemistry. *Journal of Chemical Education, 64 (7)*, 616-618.

Mystery powders. (1967). Elementary Science Study (ESS). St.Louis: McGraw-Hill.

Nussbaum, J. (1985). The particulate nature of matter in the gaseous phase. In Driver, R., Guesne, E. & Tiberghien, A. (Eds.), *Children's ideas in science*. Philadelphia: Open University Press.

Osborne, R., & Cosgrove, M. (1983). Children's conceptions of the changes of state of water. *Journal of Research in Science Teaching, 20 (9)*, 825-838.

Se're', M. (1985). The gaseous state. In Driver, R., Guesne, E. & Tiberghien, A. (Eds.), *Children's ideas in science*. Philadelphia: Open University Press.

Stavy, R. (1990). Children's conception of changes in the state of matter: from liquid (or solid) to gas. *Journal of Research in Science Teaching, 27 (3)*, 247-266.

Stavy, R. (1991). Using analogy to overcome misconceptions about conservation of matter. *Journal of Research in Science Teaching, 28 (4)*, 305-313.

Stepans, J.I. & Veath, L.M. (1994). Pupils' view of physical and chemical changes of matter. *Science Scope*, 17(8),31-35.

Swartz, C. (February, 1989). The states of matter: a model that makes sense. *Science and Children*, 20-21.

DENSITY & BUOYANCY

A.   IDENTIFICATION OF THE CONCEPTS

density, relative densities of liquids and solids, buoyancy, mass, volume and displacement, liquids, solids

B.   BACKGROUND INFORMATION FOR THE TEACHER

A small ice cube floats on water.   What about a large block of ice?   How can a little grape, weighing a few grams, sink in water but a 10 kg watermelon float? How can a drop of syrup sink in water but a gallon of oil float? How many of our students understand why a heavy person floats on water, while a small grape or a drop of syrup or a little bean sinks? And why should they?

What is density?

Why do certain things float on water while others sink? Why do large balloons go up into the air? Why, for example, no matter how much we try, some liquids mix while others won't? An important factor is the *density* of each material. *Density is the amount of material, or mass, in one cubic cm of volume of that material.* We say water has a density of 1. This means that if we take 1 ml (which is the same as 1 cubic cm or cc, the measure often used with liquids) of water and place it on a balance, it will have a mass of 1 gram. Vegetable oil, which floats on water, has a density of less than 1 gram per ml. Homogeneous materials have a definite density. For example, 1 ml of water weighs 1 gram, 10 ml weighs 10 grams, 300 ml weighs 300 grams. The ratio of grams to ml for pure water is always 1. We say the density of water is 1 gm/ml.

When we place a plastic jug filled with water in the freezer overnight, the next morning we find the container swollen and probably cracked. Water has expanded in its conversion to ice; in other words, the same amount of water (mass) now occupies a larger volume—the mass of the substance has not changed. Since the same mass occupies a larger volume, the *density* has decreased. This is the reason that ice floats on water—ice is less dense than liquid water.

What is buoyancy?

A related concept affecting the sinking and floating of solids in liquids is buoyancy. *Buoyancy is the amount of force that a fluid exerts on a solid.* This principle may be illustrated with an example. A ball of clay will sink in water; however, if made into a boat and placed carefully on water, the same piece of clay will float. In changing the shape of the clay, we keep the mass the same, but change the total volume. The boat system has a much larger <u>volume</u>, so it displaces more water than the ball. The amount of the water displaced is equal to the buoyant force exerted by water. This buoyant force is equal to the weight of the clay boat when floating , but less than the weight of the clay ball. (See Figure I.) .

Figure I

Original water level

Water only

Water with clay lump

Water with floating clay boat

C. SOME REPRESENTATIVE STUDENTS' MISCONCEPTIONS RELATED TO DENSITY AND BUOYANCY

Studies on students' science misconceptions (Stepans, et al., 1986; Clement,1987; Rowell, 1977; Shepherd & Renner, 1982; among others) give examples of students' misconceptions on density and related concepts.

♦ For an object to float it must contain air.

♦ When you change the shape of something, you change its mass.

♦ Mass (heaviness) is the <u>most important</u> factor determining whether an object will sink or float.(For example, many students believe a large block of ice will not float because it is "too heavy.") See page 54, *Liquids*.

♦ A clay ball which will sink in water will displace more water than a clay boat made out of the ball.

D. SOURCES OF STUDENTS' CONFUSION AND MISCONCEPTIONS

Density is taught by giving definitions, formulas, and historical episodes such as the story of Archimedes and the king before students have the opportunity to experience the concept.

♦ Immediate introductions of scientists' definitions and formlas are not necessarly convincing to children.

♦ Traditionally studens engage in activities after presentation and discussion about the concept.

♦ Activities tend to be verification of the formulas and generalizations already presented.

♦ Students play a passive role in the study of the concept.

♦ Just using a hands-on approach and even the traditional learning cycle is not effective in helping students overcome their naive ideas.

♦ Traditional hands-on approaches do not necessarily address the ideas and views the students bring to the class. (Smith and Anderson (1984) and Stepans, et. al. (1988)

♦ Large gaps exist between students knowing the formula for density, their ability to solve mathematical problems involving density or determining the densities of various materials, and truly making sense of specific density-related phenomena.

E.   LEARNING ABOUT DENSITY AND BUOYANCY USING THE CONCEPTUAL CHANGE MODEL

TEACHING NOTES

Provide the following materials for each small group or for groups to share:

grape	stack of paper towels
bean	masking tape
potato	ruler
ice cube	balance scale and gram masses
block of ice	3 different materials for constructing cubic boxes
cube of clay	raisins
block of clay	clear carbonated drink
saltwater solution	water colored blue
large container of water	dark syrup
graduated cylinders	vegetable oil
whole watermelon (let groups share or use as whole class demonstration)	

For best results when making the saltwater solution, use a salt with no additives, such as pickling salt.

Cubic boxes can be constructed of any three different materials, such as paper, clay, Styrofoam, or cardboard.

ACTIVITY I. Sinking and Floating of Various Objects

1. Commit to an Outcome

Given a small aquarium filled about 2/3 full of water, and materials such as: a grape, a bean, a potato, an ice cube, a bag of ice cubes (or a block of ice), a small cube of modeling clay, a small watermelon, and a large block of modeling clay, predict what will happen if you would place each of items, one at a time, in the container. Use the table provided below (Figure 1) to record your predictions. Will each object sink or float? See if you can think of the sources for your predictions or explanations.

ITEM	PREDICTION: FLOAT OR SINK?	EXPLANATION
1.grape		
2.bean		
3.potato		
4.ice cube		
5.block of ice		
6.cube of clay		
7.block of clay		
8. water-melon		
9.other		

Figure 1

2. Expose Beliefs

Share your predictions and explanations in your small group, and summarize everyone's ideas on a sheet of butcher paper. Designate a spokesperson to share the predictions and explanations of the individual members to the entire class. After everyone in the class has shared ideas and explanations, decide whether or not you want to modify your own ideas before you begin testing them.

3. Confront Beliefs

Test your ideas by placing the objects in water, one at a time. Discuss your observations with your group members. Based on you observations and discussion, do you want to make any changes in your explanations?

4. Accommodate the Concept

Based on the discussion and the testing of ideas, can you make a statement about what determines why something floats or sinks in water?

ACTIVITY II. Measuring Boxes

1. Commit to an Outcome

Make boxes that are the same size of wood, glass, and metal (or any three different materials.) The boxes should be cubes (example: 2cmx2cmx2cm). Determine the volume of each box (in cubic cm). Determine the mass of each box. List the measurements for your boxes on the table below in the column labeled "My Box".

Materials	My Box cm³	8cm³	4cm³	1 cm³
wood				
glass				
metal				
other				

Figure 2

If you had additional boxes of the same materials made in the other sizes listed on the table, what would the mass of each be? Make predictions and give reasons for your predictions.

2. Expose Beliefs

Share your predictions and explanations with the other members of your small group. Revise your ideas if necesssary after listening to other group members ideas. Select one group member to present the group's ideas and explanations to the rest of the class.

3. Confront Beliefs

Get the necessary materials to construct your first three boxes as a group. Determine the mass and volume of each and record on the table above. Construct additonal boxes to test your predictions about the mass and volume of boxes that are 1 cm cubes, 4 cm cubes, and 8 cm cubes. What can you say about the relationship of mass and volume of boxes of different sizes, but made of the same material?

Make a graph of mass compared to volume for each material , as shown in Figure 3 on the next page. Can you find the mass of 1 cubic cm of each kind of box from the graph?

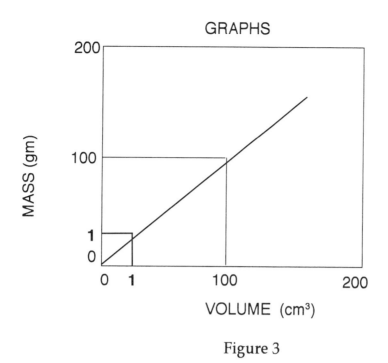

Figure 3

4. Accommodate the Concept

Make a statement comparing the masses of one cubic cm of each material. You may use the graph or the table as the basis for your statement. Use the data to write a general relationship, using any symbol appropriate to name the mass or the volume, given the other variable. Test the relationship you have written to find the volume of 100 grams of each of the materials.

5. Extend the Concept

What are some examples of the concept of density with which you are familiar?
How could you explain the following in terms of what you have observed

a) When water freezes, is it the same material? Is the mass the same? Is the volume the same? What mental models can you build to support your explanation?

b) When you drop a rock that has an irregular shape in water, what is the amount (the mass and the volume) of the water that is displaced? What would happen to the mass and the volume if, instead of water, we used a saturated salt solution? How would you explain this?

ACTIVITY III. PAPER TOWEL STACK

1. Commit to an Outcome

If you measure a stack of paper towels to determine the size (volume) and the mass of the stack, and then, after squeezing the stack together and securing it with masking tape, you measure it again, predict what you think will be affected–the mass of the stack, the volume of the stack, both, or neither?

2. Expose Beliefs

Share your predictions and your explanations with the members of your small group. Then have a representative of your group share your groups predicitons and explanation with the class.

3. Confront Beliefs

Get a stack of paper towels and other materials necessary to test your group's ideas. Revise your ideas , if necessary.

4 Accommodate the Concept

Based on your measurements, what can you say about the relationship of volume and mass of the paper towels stacks?

What changed from the 1st to the 2nd measurement: size, mass, or the material itself? What would be the mass of 1 cubic cm of the paper towels before they were taped together? After they were taped together?

5. Extend the Concept

What are some of the examples of this concept with which you are familiar?

ACTIVITY IV. A Carbonated Drink

1. Commit to an Outcome

Predict what would happen if you dropped a few raisins in a container of carbonated liquid, such as ginger ale.   Would they sink or float? Do you think the situation would change if you waited for 15-20 seconds? Give reasons for your predictions.

2. Expose Beliefs

Share your predictions and explanations, first in your small group. Then have a representative of your group present everyone's predictions and explanations of your group members to the class.

3. Confront Beliefs

Get the carbonated liquid and a few raisins and test your ideas and those of other members of your group. Based on what you see, do you want to make any changes in your thinking?

4. Accommodate the Concept

Based on the observations and the testing of your ideas, what statements can you make to explain the behavior of the raisins in the carbonated liquids?

5. Extend the Concept

What are some examples of this concept with which you are familiar?

ACTIVITY V. Liquids

1. Commit to an Outcome

You have four different liquids: water (colored blue), syrup, vegetable oil, and salt water. What do you think would happen if you poured 100 ml of the water into a graduated cylinder, then carefully poured an equal quantity of the syrup into the container? Make your individual prediction and give reasons for your prediction.

2. Expose Beliefs

Share your prediction and explanation in your small group, writing down everyone's ideas. A representative will share the predictions and explanations of your group with the entire class.

3. Confront Beliefs

Get the necessary materials (a graduated cylinder, some blue water, and some syrup and test your predictions. Discuss what happens with the members of your group and revise your ideas and explanations, if necessary, based on what you have observed.

Repeat Steps 1, 2, and 3 above with the saltwater and the syrup.

Repeat Steps 1, 2, and 3 above with the vegetable oil and the blue water.

Before you make your predictions, make some measurements of each liquid (how much mass in a given volume) or ask the teacher for data about the liquids.

4. Accommodate the Concepts

Based on the observations and the discussions, what statements can you make about the phenomena observed here?

5. Extend the Concept

What are some examples of this phenomena with which you are familiar?

ACTIVITY VI. Buoyancy

1. Commit to an Outcome

If you put a ball of clay having a diameter of about 3" (7.5-8 cm) into a container 3/4 filled with water, it will sink. If you reshape the same ball of clay to make a boat and gently place it on the water, it will float.

Individually, predict what will happen to the level of water in the container in the two situations. Which of the following possibilities will be true?

  a)   The ball will displace water, but the boat will not.
  b)   The ball will displace no water, but the boat will.
  c)   Both will displace water but the ball will displace more than the boat.
  d)   Both will displace water but the boat will displace more than the ball.
  e)   **Both will displace the same amount of water.**

Give reasons for your prediction.

2. Expose Beliefs

Share your prediction and explanation with your group members. Do you want to make any changes in your thinking after you have listened to the predictions and the explanations of others in your group? Have a representative from your group present the ideas of the members of your group to the large group.

3. Confront Beliefs

Get the necessary materials and test your ideas.

What did you notice about the water level when you placed the clay ball in the water compared to when you placed the clay boat in the water? Did your observations agree or disagree with what you thought would happen?

4. Accommodate the Concept

What statement can you make about the reason for the difference in water levels you observed?

5. Extend the Concept

What are some examples or applications of the phenomenon of buoyancy that you have witnessed?

6. Go Beyond

What additional questions or problems can you pose related to the concepts of density and buoyancy presented in these activities?

F.   REFERENCES

Clement, J. (1987). Overcoming students' misconceptions in physics: the role of anchoring intuitions and analogical validity. *Proceedings of the Second International Seminar : Misconceptions and Educational Strategies in Science and Mathematics, 3,* Ithaca, NY: Cornell University, pp.84-97.

DeVito, A. & Krockover, G. (1990). *Creative sciencing: a practical approach.*Boston , MA: Little, Brown, and Co.

Dreyfus,A.,Jungwirth,E.,& Eliovitch,R.(1990). Applying the cognitive conflict strategy for conceptual change–some implications, difficulties, and problems. *Science Education, 74(5),* 555-569.

Liem, T. (1987). *Invitiation to science inquiry.* Lexington, MA: Ginn Press.

Rowell, J.A., & Dawson , C. (1977). Teaching about floating and sinking : further studies toward closing the gap between cognitive psychology and classroom practice. *Science Education, 61(4),* 527-540.

Shepherd, D. & Renner, J.W. (1982). Student understandings and misunderstandings of states of matter and density changes. *School Science and Mathematics , 82 (8),* 650-665.

Stepans, J., Beiswenger, R.E., & Dyche, S. (1986). Misconceptions die hard. *Science Teacher, 53 (6),* 65-69.

Stepans, J., Dyche, S. & Beiswenger, R. (1988). The effect of two instructional models in bringing about a conceptual change in the understanding of science concepts by prospective elementary teachers. *Science Education, 72(2),* 185-195.

Stepans, J. (1991). Will it mix, sink or float? *School Science and Mathematics , 91(5),* 218- 220.

AIR PRESSURE

A.   IDENTIFICATION OF THE CONCEPTS
air pressure, high pressure, low pressure, Bernoulli's Principle, lift

B.   BACKGROUND INFORMATION FOR THE TEACHER

Air, whether moving or stationary, exerts pressure. Moving air, created by blowing in these activities, has a lower pressure than stationary air (Bernoulli's principle). The faster the air moves, the lower the pressure it exerts. As a result, when considering two surfaces, the *pressure exerted by stationary air is greater than the pressure of moving air* .

In the first activity, this difference in air pressure causes the paper strip and the sheet of paper to lift.   In the case of blowing under the tent, the same principle applies, causing the tent to collapse. In the case of pingpong balls, blowing between them reduces the air pressure between them; as a result, the greater outside pressure of the stationary air causes the balls to come together. Blowing through the funnel creates a lower pressure inside the funnel. The faster the flow of air, the lower the pressure. This phenomenon can be used to keep the ball spinning when you hold the funnel up and blow; also, if you hold the funnel down, you can pick up the ball by blowing through the funnel.

That airplanes get off the ground and fly is an application of Bernoulli's principle. The wings of an airplane are shaped to have a curvature. The top surface has a larger curvature than the bottom surface. As a result, the air moving over the wing has to travel a longer distance than the air beneath the wing. Since it must reach the other side of the wing at the same time, it must move faster (have a greater velocity). Because the air moving over the wing is moving faster than the air under the wing, it creates lower pressure and, consequently, a *lift* that presses the wing upward. The wings of the airplane have adjustable flaps. These are used to reduce or increase the curvature of the wing, causing greater lift during takeoff or landing.

C.   SOME REPRESENTATIVE STUDENT MISCONCEPTIONS RELATED TO AIR PRESSURE

♦   Many students believe that blowing on something always makes it move away.

♦   Some students believe that blowing takes the pressure with it.

♦   For many young learners, air neither has mass nor can it occupy space.

♦   Many children have difficulty making the connection between paper airplanes and jet airplane flight.

D.   SOURCES OF STUDENTS' CONFUSION AND MISCONCEPTIONS

Children learn from experience that when they blow on something—like a bubble or dandelion plume—it goes away. These experiences make it difficult to make sense of the fact that when you blow on a surface, it comes toward you, or that when you blow between things, they come together. These experiences make it difficult to accept the concept of Bernoulli's Principle .

♦   Air is not as tangible for many young learners as other substances. The explanations about the behavior of air and air pressure are difficult to visualize because air is usually invisible.

♦   Many textbook presentations begin with abstract concepts and terminology.

♦   Classroom presentations usually ignore students' prior views and ideas.

E. LEARNING ABOUT AIR PRESSURE USING THE CONCEPTUAL CHANGE MODEL

TEACHING NOTES

Provide the following materials for each small group:

> pieces of paper
> straws
> pingpong balls
> string
> funnel

At the end of the activities, when students are extending the concepts related to air pressure, you may want to present or discuss some of the following examples as applications of the principles:

> paper airplane flight
>
> experience of passing by a truck on the highway
>
> jets flying
>
> behavior of other fluids
>
> birds flying
>
> demonstration of crushed can (heated, sealed, then cooled)
>
> demonstration of putting a peeled hard boiled egg in a bottle using air pressure
>> (burn match in bottle with egg resting on mouth of bottle)

ACTIVITY I. A Strip of Paper

1. Commit to an Outcome

What do you think will happen if you blow over the top of a strip of paper while holding on to one end? (See Figure 1.) Give explanations for your prediction.

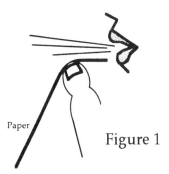

Paper

Figure 1

2. Expose Beliefs

Share your predictions and the explanations in your small group. You may draw on your own experiences and innate feelings. You do not need to agree with the other members of the group. Everyone's ideas should be summarized on a large piece of butcher paper. Choose a representative who will present all of the predictions and ideas of the individual members about the behavior of the strip of paper to the rest of the class.

3. Confront Beliefs

Get a strip of paper and test your ideas. If necessary, make modifications in your original explanations .

4. Accommodate the Concept

Based on your observations and discussions, how would you explain the behavior of the strip of paper? Share your reasoning in your small group and with the class.

ACTIVITY II. A Sheet of Paper

What would happen if, instead of just a strip of paper, you used an entire sheet of paper? Share your ideas, and then test them. Based on what you have observed in both activities, see if you can make some general statements related to the behavior of moving air and air pressure.

ACTIVITY II. A Paper Tent

1. Commit to an Outcome

Predict what would happen if you made a tent out of a sheet of paper (as shown in Figure 2 below) and used a straw to blow *into* the tent. Make your individual predictions, drawing on your experiences and give explanations for your predictions.

Figure 2

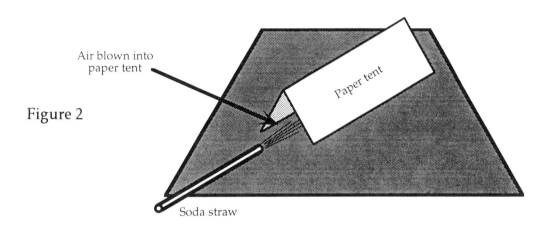

Air blown into paper tent

Paper tent

Soda straw

2. Expose Beliefs

Share your predictions and explanations in your small group and then have the group representative present the predictions and explanations to the entire class.

3. Confront Beliefs

Construct the paper tent and blow with a straw into the tent to test your predictions and explanations. Discuss what happens with your group members. If necessary, revise the explanations and ideas based on what you have observed and discussed.

4. Accommodate the Concept

Based on your observations and discussion, make a statement about the underlying principle involved here.

ACTIVITY III. Blowing Between Pingpong Balls

1. Commit to an Outcome

What do you think would happen if you used a straw to blow between two pingpong balls that are each taped to a string and hung about 5 cm apart. (See Figure 3.) Make your own individual predictions and give explanations for the predictions.

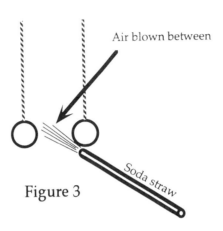

Figure 3

2. Expose Beliefs

Share your ideas in your small group and give your explanations. Remember that *all* ideas are valued and the best answers come by working with materials. You should have the opportunity to make changes in your predictions and explanation after listening to other members of the group.

3. Confront Beliefs

Get the necessary materials and test your beliefs. Based on your observations and discussions, make any necessary changes in your ideas and explanations.

4. Accommodate the Concept

Based on what you have observed and discussed, can you state a general principle about the phenomenon you observed?

ACTIVITY IV. Pingpong Ball in a Funnel

1. Commit to an Outcome

Predict what will happen if you blow through a funnel with a pingpong ball resting in it. (See Figure 4.) Specifically, how far do you think the ball will rise? Give reasons for your predictions.

Figure 4

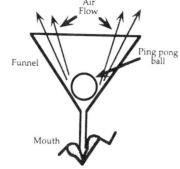

2. Expose Beliefs

In your small group, share your predictions and explanations about what would happen and why. Choose a representative to present all predictions and explanations to the large group.

3. Confront Beliefs

Get the funnels and pingpong balls and test your predictions. Based on your observations and discussions, make revisions in your explanation, if necessary.

4. Accommodate the Concept

As with the other tests, state what seems to be the general principle involved related to the behavior of objects in response to moving air.

AFTER ALL OF THE ACTIVITIES

5. Extend the Concept

In your groups discuss the connections between all of the situations presented here. What seems to be the underlying principle that explains everything you observed? Think of examples outside the classroom where you have seen phenomena and situations similar to the ones presented here and list them. A representative from your group will present to the large group applications of Bernoulli's Principle with which you are familiar.

6. Go Beyond

Think of questions and problems related to air pressure and Bernoulli's Principle you may want to pursue. Can you think of any other experiments you might want to try to test the explanations you have learned?

F.   REFERENCES

Friedl, A. (1986). *Teaching science to children—an integrated approach.* New York: Random House.

Liem, T. (1987). *Invitations to science inquiry.* Lexington, MA: Ginn Press.

LIQUIDS

A.   IDENTIFICATION OF THE CONCEPTS

behavior and properties of five common liquids: water, oil, detergent, saturated salt solution, and syrup; adhesion, cohesion, buoyancy, index of refraction, viscosity, and density

B.   BACKGROUND INFORMATION FOR THE TEACHER

What is adhesion?

What does adhesive tape do? What does the word "adhesive" mean? It implies something sticking to something else, like tape to paper, gum to a shoe, paint to a wall, or glue to wood. *Adhesion is the attraction of two different substances to each other.* Different liquids like water, oil, detergent, and syrup have different adhesive properties, as the ability of the liquid to be pulled by another liquid or other substance demonstrates.

What is cohesion?

The word "cohesion" implies togetherness, as in a "cohesive" social group. In science, *cohesion is the attraction that exists among molecules of the same kind,* as when water molecules stick together to form droplets. *Solids* have very strong cohesive forces—they are hard to pull apart. This strong cohesion keeps a brick or a tray or a table together. *Liquids* have cohesive forces, although not as strong as solids. Of the three states of matter, *gases* (the other fluid) have the weakest cohesive force. Different liquids have different forces—for some liquids, the cohesive forces are greater than for others. The fact that we can float a needle on water is because of the cohesive forces of water molecules that give it *surface tension* that resists breaking. Water has a fairly strong surface tension compared with detergent, for example, as shown in the activity with pepper.

What is density?

No matter how much you shake a container of oil and vinegar, as soon as you stop shaking, the contents become separated, with the oil standing above the vinegar. The reason is that the density of oil is much less than the density of vinegar, and denser materials tend to sink. *Density is the ratio of mass to volume.* Therefore, the densities of two materials can be compared by comparing the masses of equal volumes of the materials. For example, one milliliter of liquid A has a mass of two grams, so its density is 2 grams/milliliter. Water is an interesting liquid. It has a density of 1 gram/milliliter. We often compare other liquids to water, since it is familiar to us. The densities of common liquids such as oil, alcohol, salt water, and syrup range from .5 grams/milliliter to about 2 grams/ milliliter. (A mililiter is the same as a cm^3, which was used in the **Density** unit.)

What is buoyancy?

When we place a solid object in liquid, we must push the liquid out of the way. The liquid pushes back, in a sense, because it exerts an upward force (the *buoyant* force) on the object. The amount of force exerted by the liquid on the object depends on the amount of the liquid that is displaced. This is called *buoyancy*. The larger the volume of the solid submerged in the liquid, the more liquid is displaced and, therefore, the greater the buoyant force exerted by the liquid on the object. If the buoyant force is less than gravitational force (the weight of the object) the object sinks; otherwise, it will float.

What is viscosity?

Viscosity is a property of fluids that causes them to *resist flowing*. Molasses has a high viscosity, which means it flows slowly, whereas water has low viscosity and flows easily. The fluids whose molecules interact strongly, causing friction between them, have high viscosity. Viscosity often depends on temperature, so that liquids at higher temperatures flow more easily. The viscosity of motor oil determines its ability to lubricate the parts of an engine.

How does refraction of light occur?

Many Native Americans have been great fishermen, not because they always had expensive fishing rods and the accessories, but because they understood *refraction of light* by water. Liquids have a tendency to *bend* the light that enters them. The amount that light bends depends on the density of the medium. Water is more dense than air. When placed in a glass of water, a pencil appears broken. The reason for this illusion is that the light that hits the part of the pencil which is out of water travels only through the air and is reflected to the eye; however, for the part that is in the water, the light travels through air and then water. The fact that light goes from one medium (air) into another (water) bends the light, so when our eyes and brain perceive it, the pencil appears broken.

C. SOME REPRESENTATIVE STUDENT MISCONCEPTIONS ABOUT LIQUIDS

♦ All liquids mix.

♦ "Light" objects will float on water, while "heavy" ones will not. For example, a small ice cube will float but a large piece of ice will sink because it is heavy.

♦ Objects that float on water float on any liquid.

♦ Water atoms themselves expand or change when ice melts.

D.   SOURCES OF STUDENTS' CONFUSION AND MISCONCEPTIONS

◆   Thinking of liquids as a varied category is new to many students.

◆   Phenomena such as floating and flowing, in nearly everyone's experience, are overwhelmingly associated with water specifically.

◆   Other liquids, such as detergent and syrup, are viewed purely in connection with the purpose for which they are used and not as substances with characteristics of their own.

◆   Surface tension is an abstract concept. A film on the surface of water does nothing (perceptible) to resist an intruding finger.

◆   Floating is something that usually either happens or does not happen. It is difficult for students to conceive of a buoyant force that always pushes up and sometimes is enough for an object to float.

E.   LEARNING ABOUT LIQUIDS USING THE CONCEPTUAL CHANGE MODEL

TEACHING NOTES

Provide each small group the following materials if possible:

paper towels or napkins, cut into strips	pepper
clear glasses or cups	clay
colored water	wax paper
syrup	droppers
vegetable oil	box of paper clips
dish detergent	
saturated salt water solution	

(Make saturated solution by adding salt –1 spoonful
at a time– to room temperature water, stirring to dissolve
the salt completely. Continue adding salt until no more
will dissolve.)

ACTIVITY I: Adhesion

1. Commit to an Outcome

Predict what would happen if you placed one end of a strip of paper towel or napkin in each of the following liquids: colored water, saturated salt solution, syrup, oil and detergent. (See Figure 1.) Give reasons for your predictions. Will there be differences? If so, why do you think so?

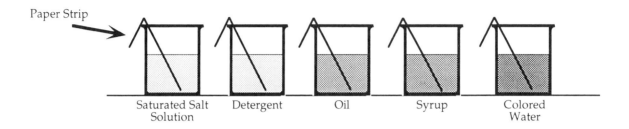

Paper Strip

Saturated Salt Solution   Detergent   Oil   Syrup   Colored Water

Figure 1

2. Expose Beliefs

In your small group, share your beliefs about what will happen if the strips of paper towel or napkin are placed in different liquids.

3. Confront Beliefs

Get the strips of paper towel or napkin and containers of colored water, oil, detergent, salt water, and syrup and test your ideas. (Use a different strip for each liquid.) Compare how far each liquid moves within a certain amount of time. Also, compare how much of the liquid moved into the paper by looking at what is left in the containers. Based on your observations, you may want to change your explanations about the abilities of the liquids to creep across the paper.

4. Accommodate the Concept

Have a member of your group write down the results of your experiments as well as all of the explanations proposed by members of your group. Your teacher will then tabulate all of the groups' results and explanations. After you have seen and heard the reports from your classmates, discuss them in your small group. Try to resolve any differences between what you expected would happen and what actually happened, and the reasons. Based on your observations and discussions, what mental model have you constructed as to the difference in the way different liquids move ?

5. Extend the Concept

What are some of the examples of this phenomenon with which you are familiar? What have learned here about why we use paper towels to clean up messes? How does nature use this creeping property of liquid? How do plants use this property to draw water?

6. Go Beyond

When out of class, try to identify questions and problems related to the creeping property of liquids and bring them to class to share.

ACTIVITY II: Cohesion

1. Commit to an Outcome

What do you think would happen if you sprinkled some pepper into water, oil, syrup, saturated salt solution, and detergent? Think of reasons (from personal experiences, common sense, or knowledge) for your predictions.

2. Expose Beliefs

Share in your small group your beliefs about what you think will happen if you sprinkle pepper on the different liquids. A representative from your group will present what the members have shared in their small groups to the large group.

3. Confront Beliefs

Get containers, each 1/2 filled with one of the 5 liquids, to test your ideas and make appropriate revisions in your thinking about the behavior of different liquids.

4. Accommodate the Concept

Share your theories about what causes the liquids to exhibit the property of cohesion. Either individually or as a group, share your model about what causes the differences in the surface tension of different liquids.

5. Extend the Concept

Can you think of examples of where you may have seen applications of cohesive forces of different liquids? How do these observations explain needles (greased) floating on water?

6. Go Beyond

Think of other questions and problems related to cohesive forces and surface tension of liquids you would like to investigate. Bring your questions and problems on surface tension of liquids to class to share with others.

ACTIVITY III: Light Refraction

1. Commit to an Outcome

Place a penny under an empty beaker or glass. Add water to the container as you observe the penny from the side. What will happen to the image of the penny?

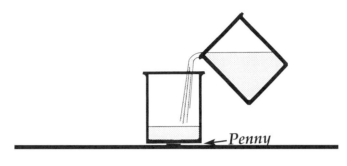

Figure 2

2. Expose Beliefs

Share in your group your ideas about what you believe will happen when water is added to a beaker containing a penny.

3. Confront Beliefs

Get a beaker and a penny and test your predictions. Check to see if you you want to make any revisions in your thinking based on what you have observed.

What did you find out? Were there any surprises? How did you feel about your observations?

4. Accommodating the Concept

How would you explain what you observed? In terms of what you have seen, can we select one idea that better explains the concept? Why?

5. Extend the Concept

What would happen if you poured oil instead of water? Detergent? Saturated salt solution? Syrup? What differences would there be, if any? Can you think of examples of where you may have seen this happen before?

In terms of what you have seen, how would you explain:

♦ why a pencil appears broken when placed in a glass of water?
♦ if you want to retrieve an object from the bottom of a pool, why do you need to reach for it where it does NOT seem to be?

6. Go Beyond

In the next few days try to think of additional examples, questions or problems you may want to pursue on the tendency of liquids to bend light .

ACTIVITY IV: Clay in Different Liquids

1. Commit to an Outcome

Predict what will happen if you place clay balls of the same size in each of the liquids (water, oil, detergent, saturated salt solution, and syrup). (See Figure 3.)

Figure 3

2. Expose Beliefs

Share with others in your group your beliefs about what you think will happen to the ball and liquid level in each case. Give reasons for your predictions. Select a representative to present to the large group the predictions and the ideas of individual members.

3. Confront Beliefs

Get five containers, each filled about 2/3 with one of the liquids (water, oil, detergent, saturated salt solution, or syrup), test your predictions and revise your explanations, if necessary.

4. Accommodate the Concept

Based on what you have observed and your discussions, what statements can you make about the result of placing the same object in different liquids?

ACTIVITY V. Clay Balls and Clay Boats

1. Commit to an Outcome

A ball of clay sinks in water, while a boat made of clay will float on water. If you have two equal size balls of clay and change one of them to a boat so that it will float on water, predict what will happen to the water in each case. Some of the options are:

    a.   when the ball sinks, the water level will not change.
    b.   when the ball sinks, the water level will rise.
    c.   when the boat floats, the water level will not change.
    d.   when the boat floats, the water level will go down.
    e.   when the boat floats, the water level will rise.
    f.   the ball (as it sinks) will displace more water than the boat.
    g.   the boat (as it floats) will displace more water than the ball.
    h.   other

Give reasons for your prediction.

2. Expose Beliefs

Share with others in your group your beliefs about what will happen to the water level when a clay ball sinks and a clay boat floats.

3. Confront Beliefs

Get the container of water and two equal size balls of clay. Change one to a boat and test your predictions. Did your observations agree with your predictions? Based on what you have seen, what changes do you want to make in your explanation?

4. Accommodate the Concept

What statement(s) can you make about the phenomenon you have observed related to the behavior of the clay ball and the clay boat when placed in water?

5. Extend the Concept

Are there examples (applications) of this phenomenon with which you are familiar?

6. Go Beyond

What additional questions, problems, or projects do you want to investigate on the effect of floating or sinking objects on the level of the liquid involved?

ACTIVITY VI: Viscosity

1. Commit to an Outcome

If we drop some of each of these liquids (water, oil, detergent, and syrup) on waxed paper with a dropper, predict which would flow faster. Explain why you think so.

2. Expose Beliefs

Share with others in your group your predictions and explanation about the ability of these liquids to flow. Have someone from your group present your predictions and explanations to the large group.

3. Confront Beliefs

Get cups of the liquids, eye droppers, and sheets of waxed paper to test your predictions and explanations about the flowing ability of these liquids. (Place your wax paper on a slanted surface to observe the drops flow. See Figure 4.) Keep track of your observations. Did they agree with your predictions? What changes do you want to make in your explanations?

Figure 4

4. Accommodate the Concept

Based on your observations and discussions, what statements can you make about the difference in the ability of liquids to flow on surfaces like waxed paper?

5. Extend the Concept

Can you think of situations with which you are familiar that make use of the viscosity of liquids? Have you seen the way catsup and syrup flow? Can you use what you have learned here to explain why we use oil in car engines and what different "oil viscosities" mean?

6. Go Beyond

Think about additional problems and projects related to viscosity. Come back and share them with the class.

ACTIVITY VII. Using mathematics to study the behavior of solids and liquids

1. Commit to an outcome

You have the following materials: colored water, saturated salt solution, vegetable oil, glycerine, and several solids made of wood, plastic, glass, and aluminum, each of a different size and shape. You also have a graduated cylinder or other narrow glass container.

a. Predict the order in which you should pour the liquids into a narrow container to have them form distinct layers.

b. Predict what will happen to each solid when dropped into the container containing the layered liquids.

Give reasons for your predictions.

2. Expose beliefs

Share your predictions and reasons for them within your group. Ask someone in your group to share these predictions and explanations with the whole class.

3. Confront ideas

In your group, plan what observations and measurements you would need to collect to make better predictions. Consider constructing tables of the data you have gathered, then graphing this data to indicate mass versus volume for each material. Then use your plan to experiment with the liquids and solids. How did your observations compare with your predictions? If there were inconsistencies, what changes would you like to make in your explanation?

4. Accommodate the concept

Based on what you have observed, negotiate an explanation for the relative densities of solids and liquids, using the data you collected and mathematical reasoning. What statements can you make about this phenomenon?

5. Extend the concept

What are some applications of using mathematics to make decisions about the behavior of liquids and solids?

6. Go beyond

What are some questions and problems you would like to pursue related to using mathematics to explain and make decisions about the behavior of materials?

ACTIVITY VIII. How many paper clips can be added to a cup that is completely filled with water?

1. Commit to an outcome

If you have a plastic cup that is completely filled with water, how many medium-sized paperclips do you think you can add to the cup before the water spills over? Write down your prediction and give reasons.

2. Expose beliefs

Share your prediction with others in your group, then have one member of the group present everyone's views to the rest of the class.

3. Confront beliefs

Get a plastic cup and fill it with water. Obtain the paper clips, then test your ideas. How did your observations compare with your predictions? If your observations are different from what you predicted, what changes would you make in your thinking?

4. Accommodate the concept

In your group negotiate an explanation for what you observe. How is this activity connected to other activities in this chapter?

5. Extend the concept

What are some examples and applications of what you have observed?

6. Going beyond

What are some new questions or problems you would like to pursue, and how would you do it?

F.   REFERENCES

Liem, T. (1987). *Teaching science to children.* Lexington, MA: Ginn Press

Stepans. J. I. (1991). Will it mix, sink, or float? (relative densities of liquids and solids). *School Science and Mathematics, 91(5),* 218-220.

FORCE, WORK, AND MACHINES

A. IDENTIFICATION OF THE CONCEPTS

force, frictional force, gravity, net force, center of mass, work, relationship of force and work, simple machines, and examples of simple machines

B. BACKGROUND INFORMATION FOR THE TEACHER

What is force?

We encounter a variety of examples of force in our daily lives, such as gravity (which we experience as weight). We experience pushes (such as when we shift gears or come to a stop in a car) and pulls (such as when a ski tow rope or someone pulls on our arm). Science uses strict definitions of many words, and so we must be clear what we mean by force. A *force* is needed to start a body moving. A force is also needed to stop a body or to change its direction if it is moving. To combine these statements, *a force is what is needed to change the speed or direction of an object.*

An object also can have forces acting upon it and <u>not</u> change speed or direction. A book resting on the table exerts a force on the table, but does not move. That is because the table is exerting a balancing force on the book. Think of it this way: if the table suddenly vanished, the book would fall. If all of the forces balance, however, the *net force* is zero and the object keeps the *same speed and direction*. In the case of the book on the table, speed is zero because of the balancing forces.

A force has both a direction and magnitude. Think about this in terms of moving a box. Suppose you just want to slide the box. First, you have to start it moving in the direction you want it to move, so you apply force in a specific direction sideways (laterally, rather than up or down). The floor tends to drag the box, which is what we call *friction*. Because of friction, you have to continue to exert a force on the box in the sideways direction to keep it moving.

What is friction?

When we push a box, we are exerting a force, and the *surface is also exerting a force in the opposite direction*. That is the force of *friction*. The smoothness or roughness of the surface material, along with the weight of the object, determines the amount of friction. Sometimes, like when we push a hockey puck along the ice, friction is very small, and the effect of our force moves the puck a long way. When we push a heavy box, however, the effect of our force does not move it a long way . *Friction is a force that does not stop pushing and always works in the direction to make things stop.* If the force of friction is large, we must continue pushing (applying force) as well in order to keep the object moving.

What is gravity?

Gravity is a force that is very much a part of our lives; in our experience, it is what makes things fall or stay down. *It is a force of attraction between the earth and every object on the earth,* including us and even tiny gaseous molecules in the atmosphere. In fact, gravity is a *force of attraction between any two objects.* Its magnitude depends on the *masses* of the objects and the *distance* between them. The larger the <u>masses</u>, the larger the gravitational force. The smaller the <u>distance</u>, the larger the gravitational force. Distance is the more important factor: if you double one of the masses, the force is doubled, but if they are half as far apart, the force is quadrupled.

What do we mean by "center of gravity" or "center of mass"?

The earth pulls downward on <u>each part</u> of an irregularly shaped object with a force equal to the weight of that part. All these separate forces can be replaced by a <u>single</u> one, equal to the weight of the entire object being pulled down at a certain point in the mass. This point is called the *center of gravity.*

What is work?

In our every day language the word "work" means physical labor. In the scientific sense, however, we equate work with what has been accomplished. *Work* is done when a force is exerted through a distance. That is, work done equals *force exerted times the distance moved.* The distance must be measured in the direction in which the force is applied. So, if we push on a car stuck in mud, we may get tired, but we have not <u>accomplished</u> anything, because the car has not moved. In a scientific sense, therefore, work has not been done.

What are simple machines?

When we hear the word machine, we may think of cars, tractors, washing machines or vacuum cleaners—things that have wheels, engines, and make noise. A *simple machine* is something that saves labor, but may not necessarily have these features. Simple machines that we use in our daily lives include: <u>pulleys, inclined planes, wheels, screws, wedges, and levers.</u> They help us to do things more easily; i.e., they help us do the *same amount of work* (movement over a distance) as if we were doing it by hand, but require us to apply *less force.* "Easiness" and "hardness" of a task in this case refer to the amount of force required.

For example, consider an inclined plane, or ramp. If we want to lift a piano into a truck, it is easier to slide it up an inclined plane because <u>less pushing force</u> is needed than if we lifted it straight up. Do we get something for nothing? No, because we also have to <u>push farther.</u> The amount of work comes out to be the same. This is an example of the use of a simple machine.

C. SOME REPRESENTATIVE MISCONCEPTIONS ABOUT FORCE, WORK, AND MACHINES

◆ Many students find it difficult to recognize the tension in a string as a force.

◆ A chair or a table cannot exert a force since it has no motion.

◆ Gravity is the same thing as air pressure.

◆ **Force has a "living" quality; i.e., objects trying to fight their way upward against the will of gravity.**

◆ Constant motion requires a constant force—if you want to keep moving along a horizontal track, you have to keep pushing, otherwise you will run out of force and just stop. This represents a failure to distinguish the role of friction as a separate force.

◆ If a body is not moving there is no force, and if something is moving, there is force acting on it.

◆ Animate objects must exert a force to hold things up, but inanimate objects do not have to do so.

◆ For many, *reaction* forces are less real than *real* forces. For example, students are told that when they hit (or exert a force on) an object, that object "exerts" a force back. It is difficult for many students to attribute an active word to a passive object.

D. SOURCES OF STUDENTS' CONFUSION AND MISCONCEPTIONS

◆ Perceptions about force and phenomena associated with force are often quite different from what actually happens.

◆ Children have their own ideas and theories about dynamics, which are often ignored by teachers.

◆ Personal experiences at home and on the playground, rather than the abstract concepts taught, are used as a basis for understanding.

♦ Children do not have experience or intuitive knowledge of the abstract notion of force.

♦ The everyday definition of work is more general and vague than the scientific definition.

♦ Many of the ideas in dynamics are abstract and anti-intuitive.

♦ In instruction, the emphasis is often on the scientific vocabulary at the expense of dealing with students' views.

♦ Children's ideas are not easily abandoned as a result of classroom demonstrations and explanations.

♦ Textbook definitions may be confusing, incomplete, or even inaccurate, because it is felt that learners, particularly the younger ones, are not capable of understanding the "whole story."

E. LEARNING ABOUT FORCE, WORK, AND MACHINES USING THE CONCEPTUAL CHANGE MODEL

TEACHING NOTES

Provide the following materials for each small group if possible:

medium-sized box (to be filled with books or other weight)
2 pieces of board for inclines, one longer than the other
materials to vary the incline surface (sandpaper, cloth, wax paper,etc.)
single pulley with rope
double pulley with rope
hammer
ruler
strong rubber band
spring scale

ACTIVITY I: The Easiest Way to Move a Load

1. Commit to an Outcome

We want to move a heavy box from the floor to the top of the table. Which of the following is the EASIEST way to do this (Figure 1)? Give reasons for your prediction.

     a. lifting the box straight up
     b. lifting the box straight up, using a pulley
     c. sliding the box up a piece of board
     d. they are all the same

Pulley

    Figure 1a.   Figure 1b.   Figure 1c.

2. Expose Beliefs

Share your predictions and reasons with the others in your group. As a group decide how you will determine "easiness." (Disregard the difficulty of setting up as you determine easiness.) Choose someone from your group to present to others the predictions and explanations of your group members.

3. Confront Beliefs

As a group, get the box, a piece of board for the incline, a pulley, rope, and stand for the pulley, and test your ideas. What did you find out? Did your observations agree with your predictions? What changes, if any, do you want to make in your thinking as a result of your observations?

4. Accommodate the Concept

Based on your observations, what statement can you make about which is the easiest way to move a box? In each case what was accomplished? What statement can you make about the relationship between what was accomplished, the distance the box was moved, and the "easiness" of moving the box?

5. Extend the Concept

What are some examples of the concept presented here? Where have you seen applications of this concept? Who may make use of this concept?

6. Go Beyond

What additional projects, questions, and problems related to doing work and the amount of "force" involved can you identify which you would like to pursue? Bring your ideas to class to share with others.

ACTIVITY II: Dragging Things on Different Surfaces

1. Commit to an Outcome

If we wanted to move the box in Activity I by pushing or dragging it up an inclined plane, which of the following surfaces would make it the easiest and which would make it most difficult to move the box? Some examples of inclined plane surfaces are: table top, cloth, waxed paper, newspaper, or sandpaper. Your teacher may have other examples. Give reasons for your choices.

2. Expose Beliefs

Share with others your choice as to which surface will be the "easiest" and which one the "hardest" over which to drag the box and the reasons for the choices.

3. Confront Beliefs

Using the method you have designed to determine the "easiness " or "hardness" of this task, get the box and a variety of surfaces and test your predictions.

What did you find out? Did your observations agree with your predictions? Make appropriate revisions in your thinking.

4. Accommodate the Concept

Based on your observations and discussion, what statement can you make about the effects of a surface on the force needed to accomplish a task?

5. Extend the Concept

What are some of the examples of this phenomenon? Where do we make use of this concept?

6. Go Beyond

Think of additional projects, questions, and problems related to friction and the relationship of type of surface and friction. Bring your ideas to class to share with others.

ACTIVITY III: Center of Mass

A. Hammer on a loose ruler

1. Commit to an Outcome

A hammer is attached to a ruler with a short rubber band. Predict what will happen if you place the ruler on the edge of the table (as shown in Figure 2). Provide reasons for your predictions.

Figure 2

2. Expose Beliefs

Share your predictions and reasons with others in your group. Have a representative from your group present to the class the predictions and explanations of the members.

3. Confront Beliefs

Get a hammer, a ruler, and a rubber band, and test your predictions in your group. You may do this several times. What did you observe? Were you surprised by what you saw?

4. Accommodate the Concept

How would you explain your observation?

B. Standing against the wall

1. Commit to an Outcome

Suppose each member of your group is standing with the right foot and shoulder against the wall (as shown in Figure 3). Predict how many members of your group will be able to take a step away from the wall with their left foot, from this position. Predict what will happen, and give reasons for your predictions.

Figure 3

2. Expose Beliefs

Share with others in your group your predictions and explanations.

3. Confront Beliefs

Taking turns in your group, test your predictions and see how many in your group will be able to take a step from the wall while they are standing against it. What did you find out?

4. Accommodate the Concept

What explanation do you have for your observation? What is the connection between this and the hammer activity in Activity III A?

C. Lifting a small chair

1. Commit to an Outcome

Predict how many members of your group will be able to stand with their heels against the wall and, without bending their knees, lift a small chair that is in front of them. Why do you think so?

2. Expose Beliefs

Share with the group your predictions and the reasons behind them.

3. Confront Beliefs

See who can lift a small chair with their heels against the wall and without bending their knees. What happened? Who was able to do it? What was the difference between those who were able to lift the chair and those who were not?

4. Accommodate the Concept

Think about the observations you made in Activities III A, III B, and III C. What do they have in common? What is the underlying principle?

5. Extend the Concept

What are some of the applications of this concept? How do we make use of this principle in various kinds of athletics and dance? How can you use what is learned here to build a mobile? Who else uses the principle of center of mass?

6. Go Beyond

What additional projects, questions, and problems would you like to pursue related to center of mass?

ACTIVITY IV: Simple Machines

1. Commit to an Outcome

As in Activity I, we want to transport a fairly heavy object from the ground to the top of the table. If we had a choice of using a short board, a long board, one pulley, or two pulleys, which one should we use (Figure 4)?   Why did you make your choice?

Short Board   Long Board

Single Pulley   Double Pulley

Figure 4

2. Expose Beliefs

Share your choice and reasons with others in your group. Have someone from your group present to the class the ideas and reasons of each individual member.

3. Confront Beliefs

In your group, test your ideas by using the method you have agreed on as to which way is best to move an object from the floor to the top of the table. What did you find?

4. Accommodate the Concept

Based on your observations and discussion, what statement can you make about the best way to move the object? What can you say about comparing the short board with the long board? What can you say about the difference between using one pulley compared to using two pulleys? What statement can you make about the role of different "simple machines?"

5. Extend Beliefs

What are some other simple machines with which you are familiar? Who uses simple machines? What are the features of an effective simple machine?

6. Go Beyond

What projects, questions, or problems about simple machines can you come up with that you would like to pursue? Bring your ideas to class to share with others in class.

F. REFERENCES

Bar, V. (1989). Introducing mechanics at the elementary school. *Physics Education, 24,* 348-352.

Freeman, I. (1965). *Physics made simple.* Garden City, New York: Doubleday & Company.

Gunstone, R. & Watts, M. (1985). Force and motion. In Driver, R., Guesne, E., & Tiberghien,A., (Eds). *Children's ideas in science.* Philadelphia: Open University Press.

Liem, T. (1987). *Invitation to Science Inquiry.* Lexington, Massachusetts: Ginn Press.

McClelland, J. A. G. (1985). Misconceptions in mechanics and how to avoid them. *Physics Education, 20,* 159-162.

McDermott, L. (1984, July). Research on conceptual understanding in mechanics. *Physics Today,* 24-32.

Maloney, D. (1990, September). Forces as interactions. *The Physics Teacher,* 386-390.

Minstrell, J. (1982, January). Explaining the "at rest" condition of an object. *The Physics Teacher,* 10-14.

Osborne, R. (1984, November). Children's dynamics. *The Physics Teacher,* 504-508.

Oxenhorn, J. & Idelson, M. (1982). *Pathways in science, the forces of nature.* New York: Globe Book Co.

Sadanand, N. & Kess, J. (November 1990). Concepts in force and motion. *The Physics Teacher,* 530-533.

Science and Children. (February 1983). Engineering a classroom discussion. 21-22.

Terry, C, Jones, G, & Hurford, W. (1985). Children's conceptual understanding of forces and equilibrium. *Physics Education, 20,* 162-165.

Watts, D. M. & Zylbersztajn, A. (1981). A survey of some children's ideas about force. *Physics Education, 16,* 360-365.

LEVERS

A.   IDENTIFICATION OF THE CONCEPTS

lever and fulcrum, relationship between weight and fulcrum distance, law of the lever, balance prediction, torque, applications of the lever

B.   BACKGROUND INFORMATION FOR THE TEACHER

What is torque, and how can it aid understanding of levers?

The action and usefulness of levers is based on *torque*, which is a rotational analog of force. With torque, an axis of rotation is always assumed. The amount of torque that results from a given force is proportional to how far from the axis of rotation that force is applied. Keep in mind the example of a door—it is harder to open a heavy door by pushing near the hinges than by pushing on the side opposite the hinges. If you are far from the hinges, your efforts are more fruitful.

How can levers be represented mathematically?

Exactly how much a greater distance from the axis of rotation can improve leverage can be calculated using a simple lever experiment. If a lever is constructed such as in Figure 1, with the weight on the left representing a constant resistance, the effect of distance can be determined by placing just enough weight on the right to balance that on the left. If you record the distance and weight of each side, and try several different locations on the right, the following relationship will emerge for a balanced lever:

$$F_1 \times D_1 = F_2 \times D_2$$

Here F_1 is the force on the left side, D_1 is the distance from the fulcrum that force F_1 is applied, and F_2 and D_2 are the corresponding variables on the right. The product ($F_1 \times D_1$) is the amount of torque counter-clockwise. To balance this torque, the product ($F_2 \times D_2$) will produce a clockwise torque. The fulcrum may be in the middle or off center.

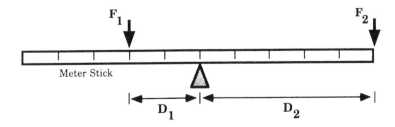

Figure 1

When there is more than one force applied on a side, each force, independent of others, produces a torque. If two forces are applied on the right and two on the left (as in Figure 2), the torques on each side are calculated and compared. If they are equal, then the lever is balanced, and we have the equation:

$$(F_1 \times D_1) + (F_2 \times D_2) = (F_3 \times D_3) + (F_4 \times D_4).$$

Figure 2

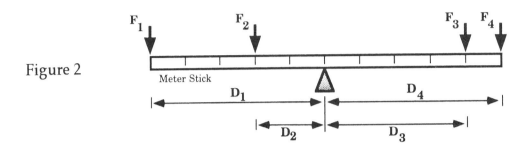

This relationship enables us to answer questions and solve problems. Note that the equations above are not true for all levers, only for levers that are balanced. In order to determine if a lever is balanced, multiply the force times the distance from the fulcrum for each weight, add together the products for the two sides, and compare the result. If the results are equal, the lever is balanced.

C. SOME REPRESENTATIVE STUDENTS' MISCONCEPTIONS ABOUT LEVERS

♦ Many students misapply the rule of levers by <u>adding</u> the force and the distance to the fulcrum on each side.

♦ In spite of having a good notion about the application of of the lever, many students have difficulty communicating applications or bringing them to the class.

♦ The closer you are to the fulcrum, the less force is needed to balance.

♦ Some students have difficulty making sense of levers because of difficulty with the concept of ratios.

♦ Some students are able to respond correctly to some of the situations, but not others, particularly when there is more than one force applied on one or both sides.

D.   SOURCES OF STUDENTS' CONFUSION AND MISCONCEPTIONS

◆   In typical instruction and reading, much emphasis is placed on rules, terms, and formulas.

◆   Making sense of the behavior of levers requires the ability to comprehend ratio and proportion, which most elementary and middle grade level students do not have.

◆   Often understanding is expected before students have a chance to explore and convince themselves of what they have been told.

E.   LEARNING ABOUT LEVERS USING THE CONCEPTUAL CHANGE MODEL

TEACHING NOTES

Provide students with simple materials to construct and test lever systems. Thin meter-sticks work well with small cylinders (such as dowels or markers) acting as fulcrums. Weights must be uniform masses such as washers, dowels, or gram masses of at least 50 grams each.

ACTIVITY: Exploring Levers

I. Situation One

1. Commit to an Outcome

Look at Figure 1 below. On the right, there are 2 weights located 3 spaces from the fulcrum, and on the left there are 3 weights located 2 spaces from the fulcrum.

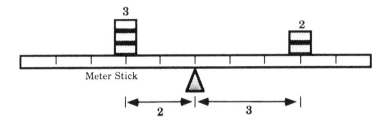

Figure 1

Predict which of the following will happen if you set up such a situation:

    a. The weights will balance.
    b. The lever will tip to the right.
    c. The lever will tip to the left.

Give explanations for your prediction.

2. Expose Beliefs

Share with others in your group your predictions and explanations as to what will happen to the lever. Have a representative from your group present to the large group the predictions and explanations of the individual members.

3. Confront Beliefs

In your group, get the necessary materials, set up the situation in the figure, and test your predictions. What did you observe? Did your observations agree with your predictions? Do you want to make any changes in your thinking about levers at this point?

4. Accommodate the Concept

Based on your observations and discussions, what statement can you make about the levers? Share your thinking with others.

II. Situation Two

1. Commit to an Outcome

Now examine Figure 2 below. On the right we have 2 weights, 4 spaces from the fulcrum, and on the left we have 3 weights, 3 spaces from the fulcrum.

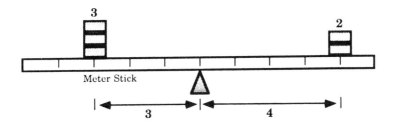

Figure 2

Predict which of the following will happen:

    a. The lever will balance.
    b. The lever will tip to the right.
    c. The lever will tip to the left.

Give an explanation for your prediction.

2. Expose Beliefs

Share with others in your group your predictions and an explanation about what will happen to the lever in this case. Have someone from your group share with the large group the predictions and reasons of your group's members.

3. Confront Beliefs

Use the weights and the lever as in the figure, and test your predictions. What did you observe? Did your observations agree with your prediction? What changes do you want to make in your thinking, if any?

4. Accommodate the Concept

Based on your observations and group discussions, what statement do you want to make about the levers? Share your statements with others.

III. Situation Three

1. Commit to an Outcome

Consider now the third case, as shown in Figure 3 below. On the right we have 2 weights, 3 spaces from the fulcrum, <u>and</u> 4 weights, 6 spaces from the fulcrum. On the left we have 7 weights, 5 spaces from the fulcrum.

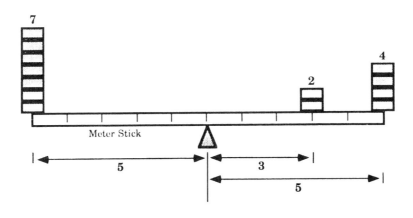

Figure 3

Predict which of the following will happen to the lever in this case:

    a. The lever will balance.
    b. The lever will tip to the right.
    c. The lever will tip to the left.

Give an explanation for your prediction.

2. Expose Beliefs

Share with others in your group your predictions and explanations about what will happen to this lever. Again, have a representative from your group present to the class the predictions and explanations of your group members.

3. Confront Beliefs

As before, test your predictions by constructing the lever pictured. Revise explanations, if necessary. What did you observe? Did your observations agree with your predictions? What changes do you want to make in your thinking?

4. Accommodate the Concept

Based on what you observed so far and your discussions, what statement can you make about what is involved in the behavior of levers? Has your explanation changed? Share your statements with others

IV. Situation Four

1. Commit to an Outcome

Look at the final figure (Figure 4). On the right we have 6 weights, 6 spaces from the fulcrum and 3 weights, 2 spaces from the fulcrum. On the left we have 3 weights, 10 spaces from the fulcrum and 4 weights, 3 spaces from the fulcrum.

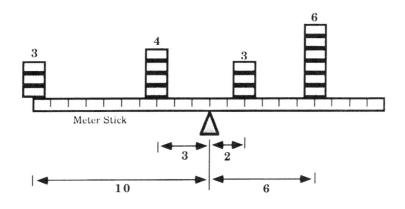

Figure 4

Predict which of the following may be true for the lever in the last figure:

  a. The lever will balance.
  b. The lever will tip to the right.
  c. The lever will tip to the left.

Provide an explanation for your prediction.

2. Expose Beliefs

Share with others in your group your prediction and explanation about what will happen to the last lever. One last time, have a representative report the views of your group members to the large group.

3. Confront Beliefs

In your group, again use the necessary weights to set up the lever as shown, and test your predictions. What did you observe? Were there any surprises? Do you want to make any changes in your thinking about what is involved in levers?

4. Accommodate the Concept

Based on your observations in all four situations, what general statement can you make about the rule of levers?

Check your general statement by applying it to each of the four situations. If it does not work, try to come up with a different rule and check that one with the weights and lever.

5. Extend the Concept

Test your rule by setting up other situations that you invent. What are some examples of this concept with which you are familiar?

Explain teeter-totters, the process of opening a door, and the operation of jack handles in terms of what you have learned here.

6. Go Beyond

What additional questions, problems, or projects would you like to pursue related to levers and their applications?

F.   REFERENCES

Clement, J. (1987). Overcoming student's misconceptions in physics: The role of anchoring intuitions and analogical validity. *Proceedings of the second international seminar: Misconceptions and educational strategies in science and mathematics. 3, 84-97.* Ithaca, NY: Cornell University.

Stepans, J. I. (1990). *Balancing.* (Unpublished document.) University of Wyoming. Laramie, Wyoming.

Zietman, A. and Clement, J. (1990). *Using anchoring conceptions and analogies to teach about levers.* Paper presented at the annual meeting of AERA, Boston, MA.

MOTION

A. IDENTIFICATION OF THE CONCEPTS

laws of motion, free fall, projectile motion, momentum, rotational motion, relative motion, and applications of laws of motion

B. BACKGROUND INFORMATION FOR THE TEACHER

What is inertia?

Stationary objects resist moving or, if they are already moving, they resist stopping. This tendency to keep their state of motion is called *inertia*. We are familiar with inertia from everyday examples: a rapidly starting car or plane pushes us back into our seat because our bodies tend to want to keep their state of motion. For the same reason, seat belts are needed in a collision to prevent us from going into the windshield.

What are force and acceleration?

"Force" is an example of a word to which scientists assign a special meaning. *A force is a push or pull.* We will learn more about force as we talk about the related topic of acceleration.

Imagine an object that is standing still. If no force acts on it, the object will remain still. This is Newton's First Law: *unless a force acts on an object, it will tend to stay at rest or in motion.* (Notice that being at rest is just a special case of motion.) However, if a force acts on the object it will accelerate, or change its speed and/or direction. If a force is constant, the acceleration is also constant. If the force on the object is doubled, the acceleration will be doubled. This is Newton's Second Law: *the acceleration of an object is proportional to the force on the object.*

What does "action and reaction" mean?

If you jump out of the front of a boat to a pier, the boat will be shoved backward. This is an example of Newton's Third Law: *for every action there is an equal and opposite reaction.* In the boat example, you are pushing on the boat in order to move your body forward to the dock. That could be considered the action. But the boat also goes somewhere: it "pushes" back on you with the same force, the reaction, and moves backward. If we jump on the ground, there is still a reaction, even though the ground does not move.

What is momentum?

Before you jump out of the boat, both you and the boat are motionless. You have zero momentum. *Momentum is the product of mass and velocity.* Since you have no velocity before the jump, you also have no momentum. But after the jump, you do have velocity (and, of course, mass) so you do have momentum. Where did it come from? It is important to notice that the boat also has momentum after the jump. Since the boat's velocity is in the opposite direction, its momentum will include a negative sign relative to the your momentum. In fact, if you carefully measure the momentum of both the boat and yourself, you will find that they are equal in size, but opposite in sign! There is still zero total momentum. (But if the boat has a larger mass, it will have a smaller absolute velocity so that the product of the two is equal.) This is called the conservation of momentum: *in any closed system, the total momentum stays the same.*

What about motion around curves?

If an object is tied to the end of string and twirled, it travels in a circular path. This is because it is acted upon by a force pulling from the center of circle through the string. The speed of rotation is related to the force that pulls on it at the center. The higher the speed, the more the force there is pulling on the object. If the speed is kept constant, the larger the radius of revolution, the greater the force. The force pulling on the twirling object is called the *centripetal* force. (See Figure I.)

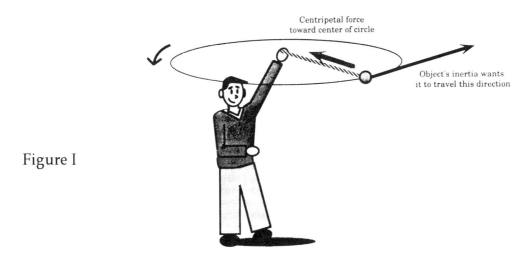

Centripetal force
toward center of circle

Object's inertia wants
it to travel this direction

Figure I

What is projectile motion?

If one throws a ball straight out from a window above the ground or if one throws the ball up from the window, in both cases the ball will have a tendency to fall. In both cases, the ball will begin to fall immediately even though in the second case it is still moving upward. It is decelerating immediately after it is released. The force on the balls is down from the release time on, even though for a little while one ball will continue to move up.

If we compare the motion of a ball that is dropped with one that is thrown straight outward at the same time, and neglect the effect of the surrounding air, the falling bodies will both

accelerate downward identically. It does not matter that one has some sideways movement. This is why the two objects, one thrown outward from a window above the ground
and one simultaneously dropped to fall freely from the same height, will hit the ground at
the same time. (This effect is the intent of the activity with the two washers, although it
will also display inertia depending on how it is hit.) The vertical and horizontal motions
are completely independent from each other. (See Figure II.)

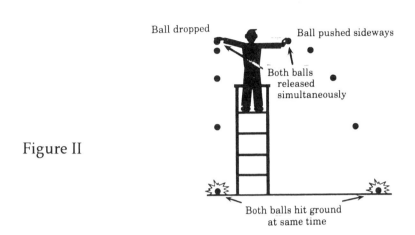

Figure II

What terms are associated with motion?

Speed is the the ratio of the distance traveled to the time elapsed to cover that distance. We
use miles per hour or meters per second (or any convenient length "per" any convenient
time) when we speak of speed. *Velocity* is the speed combined with the direction of travel.

Acceleration is the time rate of change of the velocity. If the speed and/or direction of a
body is changing, it is undergoing acceleration. Like velocity, acceleration has both a size
and a direction. *Gravity* is a constant acceleration on earth (with slight variations from
place to place). It has a value of 32 feet/second^2 or 9.8 meters/second^2, directed downward.

C.   SOME REPRESENTATIVE STUDENT MISCONCEPTIONS
ABOUT MOTION

◆   Students will say that objects fall at the same rate, because they have learned it
from a book, but they are unable to separate the additional effects of air resistance
which is needed in order to believe it that it is true.

◆   The speed of a body is directly related to the force currently applied.

◆   All things fall down, but heavy things fall fastest.

◆   The state of rest is fundamentally different from the state of motion.

◆   Constant motion requires a constant force.

♦ The amount of motion is proportional to the amount of force.

♦ If a body is not moving there is no force acting on it.

♦ If a body is moving there is a force acting on it in the direction of motion.

D. SOURCES OF STUDENTS' CONFUSION AND MISCONCEPTIONS

♦ Beliefs resulting from personal experience and "common sense" lead to student misconceptions.

♦ Instruction which fails to acknowledge students' entry level conceptions and understanding can leave students' conceptions unchanged.

♦ Instruction which fails to create the necessary conceptual conflict between students' alternate conceptions and the scientific conception can leave students' conceptions unchanged.

♦ Everyday experience suggests that objects set into motion eventually come to a stop when no obvious external force acts on them.

♦ Teachers and schools (and tests) often erroneously assume that students understand based on the <u>words</u> students use when describing phenomena associated with motion.

♦ Everyday language such as "force," which is used in a variety of broad and unscientific ways ("police force", for example), can lead to confusion on the part of the students when they hear the word used.

♦ Traditionally, these topics are taught using expository methods, with the use of routine demonstrations. The role of the student is a passive one, and they never experience a conflict between their views and the views that are being taught.

E.   LEARNING ABOUT MOTION USING THE CONCEPTUAL CHANGE MODEL

TEACHING NOTES

Provide the following materials for each small group:

drinking glass

index card

penny

toy truck (open bed)

small doll

string

book

piece of paper with same surface area as book's front cover

three equal size balls of different materials (wood, steel, glass marble)

several same size washers

table knife or ruler

dart gun with darts or syringe

section of glass tubing (10 cm long)

small rubber stopper (does not have to fit glass tubing)

Be sure to address safe behavior during Activity III B (Shooting objects.) Plan an activity area where students will be shooting objects away from other students.

ACTIVITY I: Inertia

A. Card with coin on it, resting on a cup

1. Commit to an Outcome

If you placed a penny in the middle of an ordinary index card and put them over a regular drinking glass, predict what would happen to the coin if you quickly moved the card? Explain why you think so.

2. Expose Beliefs

Share with others in your group your predictions and explanations. Have someone from your group share with the class the predictions and explanations of the members as to what will happen to the coin.

3. Confront Beliefs

For your group, get a glass, an index card, and a coin, and test your predictions. You may want to try this several times. What did you observe?

B. <u>Toy truck with a doll</u>

1. Commit to an Outcome

Suppose you have a toy truck with a flat bed, and you tie a string to the front of it. You place a little doll loosely in the bed. Predict what will happen to the doll if you pulled on the truck slowly? What do think will happen if you pulled on it quickly? Explain why you think so.

2. Expose Beliefs

Share with others in your group your predictions and explanations as to what will happen to the doll. Have a representative share the predictions and explanations of your group members with the class.

3. Confront Beliefs

Get the toy truck, string, and doll, and test your predictions.

4. Accommodate the Concept

Based on observations from the coin and the doll on the truck, what statement can you make? Did the observations agree with your predictions? Make any changes in your explanations that seem necessary.

5. Extend the Concept

Where have you seen examples of what happened here? What are the applications of this phenomenon?

6. Go Beyond

What additional questions, problems, or projects related to this would you like to pursue?

ACTIVITY II: Free fall

A. Books and paper

1. Commit to an Outcome

You have a rather heavy book, a sheet paper of the same surface area as the front cover of the book , and a crumpled piece of paper like the flat one. If dropped from the same height and at the same time, what do think will happen to these three objects?

    a.   All three would hit the ground at the same time.

    b.   The book would hit the ground first, followed by the crumpled paper and then the sheet of paper.

    c.   The crumpled paper would hit first, followed by the book and the sheet of paper.

    d.   The crumpled paper would hit first, followed by the the sheet of paper and the book.

    e.   The crumpled paper and the book would hit the ground together and the sheet will be last.

    f.   Something else will happen.

Give reasons for your predictions.

2. Expose Beliefs

Share with others in your group what you predicted and your reasons for those predictions. Choose a representative from your group to share your predictions and reasons with the class about what will happen if one drops a book, a sheet of paper, and a crumpled piece of paper.

3. Confront Beliefs

As a group, get a book and two sheets of paper of the same surface area as the cover of the book. Crumple one of the sheets of paper. Test your predictions by dropping the three objects from the same height. You may want to try this a few times. What did you observe? Do your observations agree with your predictions? If there were discrepancies, how can you explain them?

B. Three different balls

Go through Steps 1-3 of Activity A, this time using three equal size balls: wooden, steel, and glass (a marble).

4. Accommodate the Concept

What statement can you make about what happened when you dropped the book and the two sheets of paper?

What statement can you make about what happened with the balls? How were the balls the same and how were they different?

Share your statements with others in your group or the class.

5. Extend the Concept

What are some of the applications of what you saw here? Where have you seen examples of this idea in the real world?

6. Go Beyond

Think of additional questions or projects you would like to pursue on free fall.

ACTIVITY III: Projectile motion

A. Two washers, one on top of the other

1. Commit to an Outcome

Suppose you placed two stacked washers on the edge of the table so they were very close to falling off, and pushed the washer stack abruptly by striking the bottom washer with a flat object like a table knife. What do you think would happen to the washers? Provide as much information as you like. Give reasons for your predictions.

2. Expose Beliefs

Share your predictions and explanations about what will happen to the washers with others in your group. Select a representative from your group to share with others your group's predictions and explanations.

3. Confront Beliefs

Have a member of your group get the washers and a flat table knife. As a group, test your predictions and explanations. You may want to do this a few times. What did you observe? How did your predictions match your observations?

B. Shooting objects

1. Commit to an Outcome

If you shoot a cork using a syringe or shoot a dart gun at 15, 30, 45, 60, and 75 degree angles, how high will it go and how far will it travel in each trial? Make individual predictions and give reasons for the predictions about the height that the cork or dart will reach and the distance it will travel. You may make a table to record your predictions about which corks will go higher and farther.

2. Expose Beliefs

In small groups share your predictions about the projectiles and give reasons for what you predicted. Have a representative from your group present to the large group the predictions and the explanations of the group members. On the board, the teacher may tabulate the class predictions and some representative reasons you gave about the differences in the height and the distance traveled based on the angle of launch.

3. Confront Beliefs

Get the necessary materials to test your predictions about the projectile. In your group, decide how to shoot the cork or dart so that it best tests the predictions you made. After shooting the cork or dart, revise your explanations, if necessary.

4. Accommodate the Concept

How would you explain what you have seen with the projectiles? Based on your observations and discussions, write down statements and make drawings explaining the motion of a projectile and what it depends on.

5. Extend the Concept

Think of examples of projectile motion with which you are familiar. What are some examples of projectile motion? Describe the conditions necessary for the projectile to travel to the greatest height. Describe the conditions that will give the best trajectory.

6. Go Beyond

What additional questions and projects would you like to pursue about projectiles?

ACTIVITY IV: Circular motion

1. Commit to an Outcome

The diagram below shows the set-up for this activity. A piece of string about 60 centimeters long is threaded through a 10 centimeter section of glass tubing with smooth edges. Attached to the end of the string is a small rubber stopper. The string is being held down by a bent paper clip with metal washers hung from it. By holding the glass you can spin the rubber stopper fast enough so that the washers are supported and so they do not move up and down. (See Figure 1.)

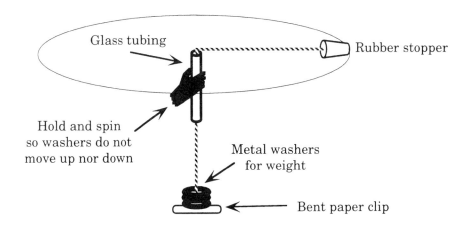

Figure 1

Predict what would happen to the speed of rotation if you kept the radius constant and increased the number of washers hanging from the string. Explain the reasons for your predictions.

2. Expose Beliefs

Share with others in your group your predictions about what will happen to the speed if you add washers and try to keep the radius constant. Also share your reasons for your predictions.

3. Confront Beliefs

In your group, get the stopper, string, washers, and glass tubing, and test your predictions. Do this several times. What did you observe? Did your observations agree with your predictions?

4. Accommodate the Concept

Based on your observations and discussions, what statement can you make about the relationship between the speed and force pulling on the object going around the circle?

5. Extend the Concept

What are some of the applications of what you have seen here? What do you predict is the relationship between speed of the object and the radius of its rotation if force (the number of washers) stays constant? Share your thoughts with others.

How would you apply what you have observed to a satellite orbiting Earth? To the motion of planets? What would be the consequences of a satellite slowing down?

6. Go Beyond

Think of additional questions and projects you would like to pursue related to circular motion.

ACTIVITY V: Balloon and straw

1. Commit to an Outcome

You have the following situation (see Figure 2): a balloon is taped to a straw and hung with a fishing line between two walls of the class. If the balloon is inflated and the mouth of the balloon is held closed(with the balloon in the middle of the fishing line), predict what will happen when it is released. Explain your prediction.

Figure 2

Soda straw taped to balloon

Walls

Balloon "Rocket" on string

2. Expose Beliefs

Share in your group your predictions and explanations as to what will happen when the balloon is released.

3. Confront Beliefs

Set up the balloon system, test your predictions, and revise your explanations if necessary. What did you observe? Did your observations agree with your predictions?

4. Accommodate the Concept

What statement can you make about what you observed here? Share statements with others in the group.

5. Extend the Concept

What are some of the applications of the balloon system? Do you know of similar examples?

6. Go Beyond

Think of additional questions and projects you want to pursue on action and reaction.

ACTIVITY VI: Bumping spheres

1. Commit to an Outcome

Suppose you have seven identical marbles hanging from strings of the same length. Predict what would happen if you pulled up one sphere and let it go. What would happen if you pulled two, three, four, five, and six of the spheres and then let them go? (See Figure 3.) Give reasons for your predictions.

Figure 3

2. Expose Beliefs

Share with members of your group your predictions and explanations as to what will happen to the spheres after they are bumped.

3. Confront Beliefs

Tape the marbles to the strings and test your predictions and explanations. What did you observe? Did your observations agree with your predictions?

4. Accommodate the Concept

What explanations do you have for your observations? What factors are involved in this activity? Share your statements with others in your group.

5. Extend the Concept

What are some of the applications of this concept?

Suppose you have five marbles, two identical large ones on the outside and three identical small ones in the middle. Suppose also that the large ones weigh twice as much as the small ones. What do you predict would happen if you pulled out a large marble and then released it? Experiment with the other configurations.

What statement can you make based on your observations and discussions?

6. Go Beyond

What additional questions and projects do you want to pursue on objects bumping into to each other?

F.   REFERENCES

Berg, T., & Brouwer, W.. (1991). Teacher awareness of student alternate conceptions about rotational motion and gravity. *Journal of Research in Science Teaching, 28(1)*, 3-18.

Eckstein, S. G., & Shemesh, M. (October 1993). Development of children's ideas on motion: impetus, the straight-down belief and the law of support. *School Science and Mathematics, 93(6)*, 299-304.

Freeman, I. (1965). *Physics made simple.* Garden City, New York: Doubleday & Company, Inc.

Friedl, A. (1991). *Teaching science to children: an integrated approach.* (Second Edition.) New York: McGraw-Hill, Inc.

Halloun, I., & Hestenes, D. (November 1985). Common sense concepts about motion. *American Journal of Physics, 53*(11), 1056-1065.

Liem, T. (1981). *Invitations to science inquiry.* (Second Edition.) Lexington, Massachusetts: Ginn Press.

Marson, R. (1978). *Motion.* Module from the Task Oriented Physical Science series, published by Ron Marson.

McCloskey, M., Caramazza, A., and Green, B. (December 5, 1980). Curvilinear motion in the absence of external forces: naive beliefs about the motion of objects. *Science, 210,* 1139-1141.

Taagepera, M., & Lewis-Knapp, Z. (Eds.) (1989). *Science demonstration lessons.* Irvine, California: University of California.

PENDULUMS

A.   IDENTIFICATION OF THE CONCEPTS

period of the pendulum; relationship of the period to mass; relationship of the period to string length, total length, and length to the center of mass; applications of the pendulum.

B.   BACKGROUND INFORMATION FOR THE TEACHER

<u>What is the period of a pendulum and what does it depend on?</u>

If the angle of motion is kept small, the *period* of the pendulum—the time it takes to swing "over and back" once—is <u>independent</u> of the mass of the pendulum bob. If we double the mass of the swinging object, the time it takes to swing over and back is unaffected. The period of the pendulum depends <u>only</u> on the distance from the point of support to the center of mass of the swinging object (Figure I). We will call this length the *effective length.*

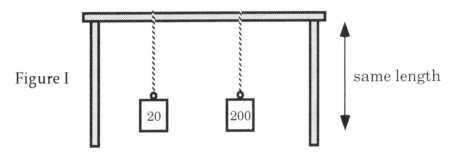

Figure I   same length

This fact runs contrary to the common intuition of many students, so here are some examples which are included in the activities for the students to explore. In Figure II, the two pendulums are made of the same mass supported by <u>strings</u> of the same length, but have different periods. Unlike what one sees in many physical science and physics textbooks, it is not just the string length of the pendulum that determines the period of the pendulum. Since the second pendulum's bob is hung vertically , it has a lower center of mass; therefore, it has a greater effective length and a longer period — it takes longer to swing over and back.

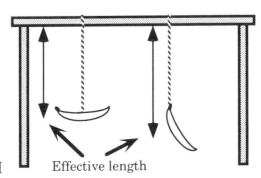

both strings
same length

Both bananas
same size, shape,
weight, etc.

Figure II   Effective length

Similarly, in Figure III, the two pendulums have the same total length, but again differ in effective length because the second pendulum has a higher center of mass. In this case, the left pendulum will have a longer period.

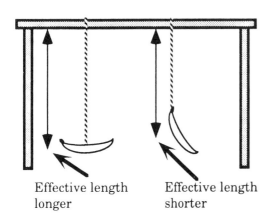

same <u>total</u> length

Different centers of mass

Effective length longer

Effective length shorter

Figure III

<u>How is the period of a pendulum expressed mathematically?</u>

Mathematically, the time that takes for the pendulum to make a complete swing (again, this is called the period) is given by the formula

$$T = 2\pi \sqrt{(l/g)}$$

where T is the period, π is the numerical constant (= 3.14), l is the effective length of the pendulum, and g is the acceleration of gravity ($g = 980$ cm/s^2). g is in cm/s^2, l is measured in cm, and T is in seconds.

(Note: period is a difficult concept for many young learners. In order to simplify the language, the questions in the activities are phrased in terms of "which one goes faster." While the speed with which a pendulum swings over and back is related to the period, it is <u>not</u> an equivalent measure. If, however, two pendulums are released at the same time and from the same angle, asking which one goes "faster" is a way to compare the periods. This is what we have done.)

C.   SOME REPRESENTATIVE STUDENT MISCONCEPTIONS ABOUT PENDULUMS

◆   Mass ("weight") is the primary factor determining the period of a pendulum.

◆   Some students will believe the pendulum with the lighter bob moves faster while others will believe the heavier one will move faster.

◆   The period of the pendulum is often confused with the speed of the pendulum. In fact, the speed depends on both the effective length and the angle of deflection.

◆   The string length alone is the important contributor that determines the period of the pendulum.

◆   What the pendulum is made of determines the period of the pendulum.

◆   The period of the pendulum is the same as how long it swings before it stops.

◆   The shape of the pendulum determines its speed.

◆   Some students cannot distinguish the effects of gravity, air resistance, and friction from factors that affect the period of the pendulum.

D.   SOURCES OF STUDENTS' CONFUSION AND MISCONCEPTIONS

◆   Textbook presentations are often abstract and move quickly through terms and formulas without exploration. For example, we often use conservation of energy to start with, giving the formula $mgl = 1/2\,mv^2$. We then divide both sides by m and solve for v to get $v = \sqrt{2\,g\,l}$. Our purpose in doing this is to show that the speed is independent of the "heaviness" of the pendulum, but this is not easily accepted by most of the students.

◆   Pictures in textbooks and other instructional materials can be misleading.

◆   Personal experience and innate feelings can seem to contradict what students read and are told.

◆   Arguments contradicting misconceptions are often purely mathematical, and simply are not convincing to students.

E. LEARNING ABOUT PENDULUMS USING THE CONCEPTUAL CHANGE MODEL

TEACHING NOTES

If possible, provide the following supplies for each small group:

>   steel sphere and wooden sphere (same size)
>   wooden cylinder (3–4 cm in diameter and 8–10 cm long)
>   strong thread
>   cellophane or masking tape (to tape bobs to thread if bobs do not have holes)
>   centimeter ruler or meter stick

ACTIVITIES: PERIOD OF THE PENDULUM

ACTIVITY I. Pendulums with the Same Length but Different Mass

1. Commit to an Outcome

Consider two equal-length pendulums, one with a wooden ball for a bob and one with a steel ball as a bob. (See Figure 1 below.) Clearly, the steel ball is more massive than the wooden ball.

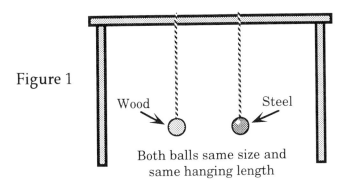

Figure 1

Wood   Steel

Both balls same size and
same hanging length

Predict what will happen if the two pendulums are set in motion at the same time. Which of the following is true for the <u>first few</u> swings (3-4):

    a. The wooden ball will swing faster (make more swings in a given time).
    b. The steel ball will swing faster (make more swings in a given time).
    c. They will have the same speed (make the same number of swings in a
       given time).

Make individual predictions and give explanations for the predictions.

2. Expose Beliefs

Share your predictions and explanations about the two pendulums. After listening to the predictions and the explanations of others in the group, do you want to make any changes in your thinking? Select a representative to present the predictions and explanations of the members of the group to the large group.

3. Confront Beliefs

Get the bobs and string and set up the pendulums to test your predictions. Rethink your explanations, if necessary. You may want to do this several times and have different people count periods (to 3-4) of the different pendulums. Remember we are looking to compare the *period* of the pendulums — which will go over and back faster?
What did you observe? How did your observations compare with your explanations?

4. Accommodate the Concept

Based on your observations and discussions, what statement can you make about the period of pendulums with equal string length and equal size bobs, but with one bob being much heavier than the other? Share your statement(s) with others in the group.

5. Extend the Concept

Can you think of other examples of equal size pendulums with different masses?

ACTIVITY II. Pendulums with the Same String Length but Different Shapes

1. Commit to an Outcome

Shown in the Figure 2 below are two pendulums, hung from strings of the same length. Notice that the bobs have different shapes. One is a wooden sphere, as before, while the other is a wooden cylinder.

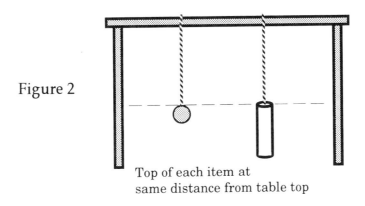

Figure 2

Top of each item at
same distance from table top

If the two are released at the same time, which of the following will happen? Give reasons for your predictions.

      a. The sphere will swing faster.
      b. The cylinder will swing faster.
      c. The two will have the same speed.

2. Expose Beliefs

Share your predictions and explanations with others in your group about what will happen to the two pendulums. Have a representative from your group share the predictions and explanations with the members of the class.

3. Confront Beliefs

Get the sphere, cylinder, and string, and set up the two pendulums. As before, test your predictions by counting 3-4 swings over and back and finding out which pendulum gets there first. Again, you may want to do this several times.

What did you observe? Did your observations agree with your predictions?

4. Accommodate the Concept

Based on your discussions and observations of the sphere and the cylinder, what statement can you make about the period of pendulums with equal string length but different shapes?

Do you want to make any changes in your statement from Activity I based on what you have observed and discussed here?

5. Extend the Concept

What are some of the applications of what you have observed here? Can you think of examples related to these applications?

ACTIVITY III. Pendulums with the Same TOTAL Length

1. Commit to an Outcome

In Figure 3 below, there are two pendulums with equal total lengths; in other words, the distances from the points of suspension to the bottom of the bobs are the same. As before, the bob of one is a wooden sphere, and the bob of the other is a wooden cylinder.

Figure 3
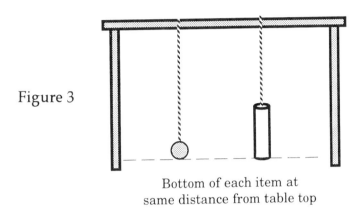

Bottom of each item at
same distance from table top

Again, predict which of the following will happen if the two are released at the same time and give reasons for your predictions.

    a. The sphere will swing faster.
    b. The cylinder will swing faster.
    c. The two will have the same speed.

2. Expose Beliefs

Share with others in your group your predictions and explanations as to what will happen if we swing two pendulums of equal total lengths.

3. Confront Beliefs

In your group, test your predictions about the periods of two pendulums with equal total lengths. What did you observe? Did your observations agree with your predictions? Do you want to make any changes in your thinking?

4. Accommodate the Concept

Based on your observations and discussions, write down a statement about the period of two pendulums which have different shapes but equal total length. Utilizing your observations and discussions from Activities I, II, and III, what statement can you make about factors which determine or do not determine the period of a pendulum?

5. Extend the Concept

What are some of the examples related to this with which you are familiar? Can you think of applications of this phenomenon?

ACTIVITY IV. Pendulums with the Same Length to the Center of Mass but Different Masses and Different Shapes

1. Commit to an Outcome

Consider Figure 4. There are two pendulums with different total lengths and different string lengths, but the distance from the top (the point of suspension) to the center of the masses is the same. Again, the bob of one is a wooden sphere, and the bob of the other is a wooden cylinder.

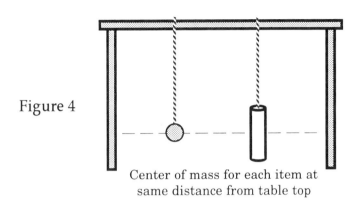

Figure 4

Center of mass for each item at same distance from table top

Once again, predict which of the following will happen if the two are released at the same time and give reasons for your predictions.

  a. The sphere will swing faster.
  b. The cylinder will swing faster.
  c. The two will have the same speed.

2. Expose Beliefs

Share with others in your group your predictions and explanations about the period of these two pendulums where the distance from the point of suspension to the center of mass is the same.

3. Confront Beliefs

In your group, set up the two pendulums and test your ideas. You may repeat this several times. What did you observe? Did your observations agree with your predictions?

4. Accommodate the Concept

Incorporating your observations from all four situations, write a cumulative statement about what you think is the determining factor affecting the period of a pendulum. Share your statements with others in class.

5. Extend the Concept

Share examples and situations related to what you have learned here. What are some of the applications of what you have observed and discussed? What are some of the examples that you have encountered in your own lives or in other classes? Pendulums are common, and you may bring up any situation that is familiar to you.

6. Go Beyond

Think of other questions or problems related to pendulums that you may be interested in pursuing outside the class.

ACTIVITY V. The algebra of the pendulum

1. Commit to an outcome

Predict how the *period* of a pendulum (the time it takes for the pendulum to make a complete swing) varies with the *effective length* (distance from the point of suspension to the center of mass). Give reasons for your predictions.

2. Expose beliefs

Share your predictions and explanations within your group. Ask someone from your group to present the ideas of the individual members to the class. In your group decide how to set up the activity and collect the necessary data.

3. Confront beliefs

Get the materials you need to carry out the plan you designed. Perform the test and record your data. Be sure to do multiple tests.

4. Accommodate the concept.

Put your data in the form of a table, then graph the data using appropriate units. What statements can you make about how the period of a pendulum varies with its effective length? Using the data, express this as an algebraic relationship.

5. Extend the concept

What are some applications and extensions of what you observed?

6. Go beyond

What are some new questions or problems you would like to pursue, and how would you do it?

F.   REFERENCES

Stepans & Hutchison (1998). *Challenging Students to DO Meaningful Mathematics.* **Clearwater, MN: Sciwood Publishing.**

Elementary science study. Pendulum. (1969). New York: McGraw-Hill.

Stepans, J.I. (1990).   Using the pendulum to illustrate the conceptual change teaching strategy. *(unpublished document).* University of Wyoming, Laramie.

ELECTRICITY

A.   IDENTIFICATION OF THE CONCEPTS

electricity; complete circuits; short circuits; parallel and series circuits; relationship of current, voltage, and resistance; insulators; conductors

B.   BACKGROUND INFORMATION FOR THE TEACHER

What is a complete circuit?

In these activities, a complete circuit consists of a battery, a light bulb, and a wire. As long as one pole of the bulb is connected (with a wire or other *conductor* of electricity) to either the positive or negative pole of the battery and the other pole of the bulb is connected to the other battery pole, the circuit is complete and the light bulb will light. The battery is the *voltage source*, providing the electrical energy. It drives a current through the conductor and the light bulb. When the current passes through the light bulb (a *resistor*), light and heat result.

How are voltage, current, and resistance related?

The relationship between voltage (V), current (I), and resistance (R) is summarized in the formula $V = R \times I$. In other words, when the resistance (from the light bulb) is multiplied by the current, the product is the voltage (from the battery).

What are series and parallel circuits?

In a series circuit, the resistors follow each other, as in Figure I, where light bulbs act as resistors. In this arrangement, each resistor adds its value to the total resistance of the circuit. As we add resistors in series, the total resistance increases, and, if we keep the voltage constant by using the same number of batteries, the current decreases. The lower current can be observed by the dimming of the light bulbs. Note, however, that since the resistors are all in line, the amount of current passing through one of them is the same as the amount passing through all of the others.

Figure 1

In a parallel circuit, resistors are not added end-to-end, but are added so they create <u>two</u> paths for the current to follow, as in Figure II, where, again, light bulbs act as resistors. Adding more resistors in this arrangement actually decreases the total resistance. The current that results from the battery is split between all the resistors, and the amount of current going through each of them can be different. If all resistors in parallel are equal, the current will also be split, and will be equally shared among them. If the difference between two parallel resistors is very large, most current flows through the smaller resistor and not through the larger one. (This is what some people call the "path of least resistance.") An extreme example of this phenomenon is an *electrical short*, where the current travels an unintentional path of least resistance, usually causing trouble.

Figure II

What are conductors and insulators?

Since the 18th century, it has been known that materials can be divided into two categories based on their ability to carry an electric current. Those that carry an electrical current easily, such as gold, copper, aluminum, or salt water, are appropriately called *conductors*. Those that do not carry an electric current, such as glass, wax, wood, and distilled water, are called *insulators*. Physically, the difference between conductors and insulators is this: in conductors, charge carriers are present and free to move, while in insulators they are not. For example, metals have electrons that are free to move throughout the metal; salt water has ions that are also free. In pure water, there are no free ions, so it will not conduct electricity. The same is true of other insulators, such as wood and plastic. Although there is variation in how well a material conducts or does not conduct, almost all materials fall clearly into one of these two categories.

C. SOME REPRESENTATIVE STUDENT MISCONCEPTIONS ABOUT ELECTRICITY

♦ Batteries store a certain amount of current. This current is consumed by any appliances or lights connected to it.

♦ Current leaves the battery from one terminal, but since some is "used up", less returns to the other terminal.

♦ If current passes through a number of identical resistors in series, each successive one will receive a smaller share.

♦ In a series circuit, current is shared among resistors.

♦ Current, energy, voltage, and power are all the same.

♦ "Negative current" goes back to the battery. "Positive current" comes from the battery.

♦ The positive pole of the battery makes current go to the light bulb, where the current is made negative.

♦ If wires are connected to a battery and bulb, no matter where, a complete circuit is made.

♦ A given battery releases the same amount of current to every circuit.

♦ If a bulb is farther away from the battery, it will be dimmer.

D. SOURCES OF STUDENTS' CONFUSION AND MISCONCEPTIONS

♦ Common analogies, like water in a pipe or blood flowing through vessels, can cause difficulty because the similarity is not complete. For example, pipes and veins are hollow, but wires are not.

♦ Instructional materials are often not ideal. Most often materials such as light bulbs were made to be light bulbs rather than as tools for teaching.

♦ Current is not an appropriate concept for many young learners.

♦ The scientific model of current is not a fundamental concept.

E. LEARNING ABOUT ELECTRICITY USING THE CONCEPTUAL CHANGE MODEL

TEACHING NOTES

Provide the following materials for each small group:

> 2 or more batteries
> 2 or more bulbs (1.25 V or 1.50 V)
> bulb holders
> battery holders
> copper wires
> aluminum wires
> chalk
> string
> salt water
> baking soda solution
> small rock
> piece of wood (pencil, dowel, craft stick)

For Activity IV (Batteries and Bulbs), you may provide commercial materials for constructing batteries and bulbs. Most science equipment companies distribute kits for making D cell batteries. Nichrom wire can be used as a filament in constructing model bulbs. However, you may choose to have students refer to textbooks, encyclopedias, or other reference materials to compare their mental models of batteries and bulbs to other models. Remind students that it can be dangerous to open real batteries without a knowledgeable adult to help them.

ACTIVITY I: Making a Circuit

A. Lighting a bulb

1. Commit to an Outcome

If you had wires, batteries, and a light bulb, do you think you could connect them in a way that would light the bulb? If you think you could, make a drawing of the set-up you would create, using the least number of batteries and wires to light the bulb. Explain your reasons for the way you made your drawing. Also, are there other ways to connect the items to light the bulb? If you think it is not possible to light the bulb, give some reasons and tell what else might be needed to light the bulb.

2. Expose Beliefs

In your small group, share your ideas, including your drawings and explanations about how the components should be connected to light the bulb. Your group representative will present to the entire class the ideas, drawings of the set-up, and explanations of your group members.

3. Confront Beliefs

Using batteries, wires, and light bulbs, test your ideas and those of your group members.

B. Which circuits work?

1. Commit to an Outcome

Look at the 12 drawings on Prediction Sheet #1. Predict which of the bulbs in the drawings will light and which ones will not and give reasons for your decisions.

2. Expose Beliefs

Share your ideas and explanations with your group members. Your group representative will present your group's ideas to the class.

3. Confront Beliefs

Get the necessary materials and test your predictions. Then decide if, based on your tests, you want to make any changes in your thinking related to the electrical set-ups. What could be done to light the bulbs that did not light when you tried them? Test your ideas.

4. Accommodate the Concept

Based on what you have seen in these first two activities, what statement or statements can you make about what is needed to light a bulb? What conditions are necessary for a circuit to be completed? What does "electrical short" mean to you?

5. Extend the Concept

Can you give examples of where we use electrical circuits? What would happen if in one of the ituations where the light bulb did light, we introduced another wire connecting one pole of the battery to the other? Where do electrical shorts occur in our daily lives? What are some of the things which may happen when there is an electrical short?

6. Go Beyond

Between now and the next session, think of other examples, questions, or problems on the topic of complete circuits and electrical shorts, and bring them to class to share.

Caution: Electrical outlets at home and in school carry a large amount of electricity and are extremely dangerous. NEVER insert wires or other materials into outlets. Use batteries, such as the ones used here in class, if you want to try any activities at home.

PREDICTION SHEET 1. Will the bulb light?

If you think the bulb will not light, say why not.
After you have made your predictions, test them.

ACTIVITY II: Lighting Two Bulbs

A. Constructing a two bulb circuit

1. Commit to an Outcome

Using the least number of batteries and wires, make a drawing of set-ups that will light two light bulbs at the same time. Think of different ways to do this and draw them. Provide reasons for your drawings and explain if there will be a difference in the outcome with the different set-ups. If so, why?

When you have a circuit that you believe will light the two bulbs, decide whether there will be a difference in the brightness of the bulbs and think of a reason why.

2. Expose Beliefs

Share your drawings and explanations in your small group and have your representative present everyone's ideas to the large group. Be prepared to ask clarifying questions or answer questions from others.

3. Confront Beliefs

Get the necessary bulbs, batteries, and wires, and test your ideas by connecting them in the different ways. Do you notice a difference in brightness of the bulbs when they are connected in a different way?

B. Which two bulb circuits will work?

1. Commit to an Outcome

On Prediction Sheet #2, predict whether the light bulbs will light. If so, why? If not, why not? Also, in each case that you believe the bulbs will light, predict what will happen if one of the bulbs is unscrewed and removed from the set-up. Give reasons for your predictions.

2. Expose Beliefs

Share your predictions and explanations with your group members. After listening to their ideas, do you want to make any changes in your own thinking? Have someone from your group present to the class the predictions and reasons of each member.

3. Confront Beliefs

Get the bulbs, wires, and batteries, and test your ideas by setting up the circuits as on the prediction sheets. For the set-ups that you predicted would not light the bulbs, what can you do to make them light? Test your ideas.

4. Accommodate the Concept

From what you have learned in the two parts of this activity, what statements can you make about electrical circuits that have more than one light bulb? Why is there a difference in the brightness of the bulbs when they are connected differently? What happens in each case to the brightness of the remaining bulb when you remove one bulb? Can you think of other analogies where this may be true? What do we call different kinds of circuits?

5. Extend the Concept

Where do we use different circuits? What experiences have you had with parallel and series circuits?

6. Go Beyond

For the next session, bring other examples, questions, and problems on electrical circuits that you may be interested in pursuing.

Caution: Electrical outlets at home and in school carry a large amount of electricity and are extremely dangerous. NEVER insert wires or other materials into outlets. Use batteries, such as the ones used here in class, if you want to try any activities at home.

Prediction Sheet 2. Will the bulb(s) light?

If you think the bulb will not light, say why not.
After you have made your predictions, test them.

ACTIVITY III: Insulators and Conductors

1. Commit to an Outcome

Predict which of these materials—copper wire, aluminum wire, chalk, string, water, salt water, baking soda solution, rock, and wood—will complete an electrical circuit and which ones will not. Give reasons for your decisions.

2. Expose Beliefs

Share your predictions and explanations about which materials will complete a circuit with others in your group. Your group representative then will present your group's predictions and explanations to the large group.

3. Confront Beliefs

Get the materials, and, with your group members, test your ideas on whether each material is a conductor or insulator of electricity. Based on your observations, are there any changes you want to make in your ideas about what is a conductor and what is an insulator of electricity?

4. Accommodate the Concept

Based on your observations and discussions, how would you classify conductors and insulators of electricity? What are the advantages of certain conductors over others? What are the criteria for a GOOD conductor? a GOOD insulator? If you were to build a mental model of the inside of a conductor, how would it be different from the inside of an insulator? How do textbooks present the inside of conductors and insulators? How does the textbook's explanation compare with your own mental model?

5. Extend the Concept

How do we make use of the ideas of conductors and insulators in our daily lives? What are some other examples of conductors and insulators we use in our homes?

6. Go Beyond

What other examples of conductors and insulators can you locate? Is there a project or experiment related to conductors and insulators you would like to try? Bring your questions, problems, and ideas to class to share.

Caution: Electrical outlets at home and in school carry a large amount of electricity and are extremely dangerous. NEVER insert wires or other materials into outlets. Use batteries, such as the ones used here in class, if you want to try any activities at home.

ACTIVITY IV: Batteries and Bulbs

1. Commit to an Outcome

a) Make a mental model of how a battery works. Share with others in your group.

b) What materials do you think you would need to make a battery? Make a list and explain why each component would be needed.

c) What materials do you think you would need to make a light bulb? Make a list and explain why each component would be needed.

d) If you had the materials, how would you put them together to build a battery? A light bulb? Include drawings with your explanations.

2. Expose Beliefs

Share your drawings and explanations of your models for building the battery and the light bulb with your group. Discuss the pros and cons of different models. You do not have to agree with others in your group on what it takes to build a battery and a light bulb.

3. Confront Beliefs

There are various ways you can test your ideas about what batteries and light bulbs are made of. You can get the necessary materials to build and test them or you can get into a battery and light bulb and examine how each is made. You can also refer to written materials and compare your ideas with those appearing in books.

Caution: Many batteries contain acid. You should not open any battery without consulting a knowledgeable adult and wearing safety glasses and gloves.

4. Accommodate the Concept

What are the principles behind the operation of the three components of the circuits you have worked with (battery, conductor, and light bulb)? What makes a battery a source of energy? What makes a material conduct electricity? What makes a light bulb create light and heat when connected to a battery via conductors?

5. Extend the Concept

How is the electricity used at home or at school the same as or different from the electricity observed and discussed here in class? How is the source of electricity at home different from a battery? Are the electrical conductors used at home the same or different from the ones we have used here? Are the light bulbs used at home the same or different from the ones used in class? What makes the electrical outlets at home dangerous, while the electricity you worked with in class was safe?

6. Go Beyond

Think about the different concepts covered here. You may work on projects dealing with electricity at your own convenience. You may want to set up a demonstration about one of the concepts that we covered here to share with others

Caution: Electrical outlets at home and in school carry a large amount of electricity and are extremely dangerous. NEVER insert wires or other materials into outlets. Use batteries, such as the ones used here in class, if you want to try any activities at home.

F. REFERENCES

Elementary Science Study. (1968). Batteries and bulbs. New York: McGraw-Hill.

Fredette, N. and Lochhead, J. (1980). Student conceptions of simple circuits. *The Physics Teacher, 18,* 194-198.

Heller, P. M. and Finley, F. N. (1992). Variable uses of alternative conceptions: A case study in current electricity. *Journal of Research in Science Teaching,* 29(3), 259-275.

Shipstone, D. (1985). Electricity in simple circuits. In Driver, R., Guesne, E., & Tiberghien, A.,(Eds.), *Children's ideas in science,* (33-51). Philadelphia: Open University Press.

Shipstone, D. (1988). Pupils' understanding of simple electrical circuits. *Physics Education, 23,* 92-96.

MAGNETISM

A.   IDENTIFICATION OF THE CONCEPTS

magnetism, magnetic fields, kinds of magnets, magnetic materials, magnetic force, relationship between electricity and magnetism, materials through which magnetism penetrates, magnetic strength

B.   BACKGROUND INFORMATION FOR THE TEACHER

What is magnetism?

The Chinese discovered that a splinter of rock called magnetite (lodestone or loadstone), if hung freely, would always set itself in a north-south direction. This behavior remained a mystery for centuries before scientific explanations came about in the 1800s. Now countless applications of magnetism are employed in homes and at work.

Magnetism comes from the special arrangement of atoms in certain materials. Everything is made of atoms, and each atom has its own tiny, intrinsic magnetic field. In materials such as rubber, paper, plastic, and ordinary rock, the atoms have no particular arrangement, so all of the atomic magnetic fields cancel each other out and produce no overall magnetic quality. In iron, however, the individual atoms are magnetized strongly enough to line up in tiny groups called *magnetic domains*. Depending on how aligned these magnetic domains are with one another, iron can be nonmagnetized or completely magnetized. This property is seen when an external magnetic force, such as that of a magnet, is brought near to iron filings, causing the magnetic domains to line up.

What different kinds of magnets are there?

Magnets can be *permanent* or *temporary*. Permanent magnets retain their magnetic property for a period of time. Temporary magnets are those in which the magnetic force can be turned off and on by removing the source of energy that causes the material to become magnetic, such as an electric current in the case of an electromagnet. Bar magnets are permanent magnets, but if heated, dropped, or placed in a strong magnetic field, they can lose their magnetism. Permanent magnets can be made by stroking hard steel repeatedly with a magnet.

Some examples of common permanent magnets are bar magnets, horseshoe magnets, disk magnets, and cylindrical magnets. Without actually testing, you cannot tell how strong a magnet is. For example, bigger magnets are not automatically stronger than smaller magnets, nor are certain kinds of magnets always stronger than certain other kinds.

<u>What is an electromagnet?</u>

A loop of wire that carries an electric current has a magnetic property and creates around it a magnetic field. The stronger the current and the greater the number of windings in the coil, the stronger the field and hence the stronger the electromagnet. An electromagnet may be constructed with bell wire wound around a large iron nail and connected to the poles of a battery. (See Figure I.)

Figure I

<u>What distinguishes magnetic materials from non-magnetic materials?</u>

There are a limited number of materials that can be magnetized or be attracted to a magnet. Magnetic materials have the ability to align their atoms into non-canceling magnetic domains. Most of these materials are metals. They include iron, nickel, cobalt, and many mixtures (alloys) of these. Other materials, including metals such as aluminum and copper, are not magnetic.

<u>What is a magnetic field?</u>

If you set one magnet on the table and bring another magnet close to it, you will feel a magnetic force. All magnets have a surrounding region where their effects can be felt, though some are stronger than others. This region is called *magnetic field*. The field is strongest near the magnet and decreases as it extends into the surrounding space. The direction and the magnitude of the field may be illustrated by *field lines*—imaginary lines which connect points of equal magnetic strength. The closeness of the lines to each other indicates the strength of field. (See Figure II.)

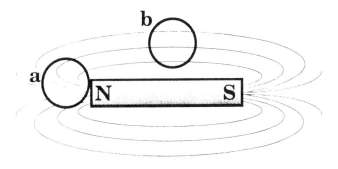

Figure II

The field lines are closer in a than in b, therefore, the field is stronger there.

<u>What materials can magnetism pass through?</u>

A simple permanent magnet will produce a field that can be detected with a small compass. Some simple tests can demonstrate that magnetism will pass through paper, wood, some kinds of sheet metal, and many other materials. Be sure to have some idea of the range of your magnet before you start testing; distance will rapidly diminish the effect of any magnet. (And be careful not to let the magnet get too close to computer disks, magnetically coded library books, or recording tapes!)

C.   SOME REPRESENTATIVE STUDENT MISCONCEPTIONS ABOUT MAGNETISM

◆   The size of a magnet determines its strength.

◆   All metals are attracted to magnets.

◆   All silver colored items are attracted to a magnet.

◆   While magnetism may be able to pass through paper, it cannot pass through wood, a notebook, a table, or other thicker materials.

◆   Only magnets can produce magnetic fields.

◆   A magnetic field is a two-dimensional pattern of line surrounding a magnet, not a three-dimensional field or force .

◆   Magnetic field lines exist only outside the magnet.

D.   SOURCES OF STUDENTS' CONFUSION AND MISCONCEPTIONS

◆   It is difficult for students to accept that aluminum, for example, a metal that seems very much like iron, is not attracted to a magnet.

◆   Materials such as a stack of paper, wood, plastic, and glass are tangible barriers, unlike air. It is difficult for students to accept that magnetic fields can penetrate these tangible barriers.

◆   Textbook wording, such as "transparent to magnetism," may create confusion in students. 'Transparent' means 'see through' to most students, and materials such as wood clearly do not have this property. This example also might seem to imply that magnetic properties can be *seen*.

♦ Quickly connecting magnetic properties to atomic properties may be inappropriate for many young learners.

♦ The rapid transition from the idea of a magnetic rock to metal magnets that occurs in many traditional presentations may cause confusion.

♦ The statement that magnetic lines of force "go through" materials may be difficult for many to accept.

♦ Ideas are often <u>imposed on</u> children, rather than allowing them to have the opportunity to <u>make sense</u> of something by exploring and making models over time.

♦ The notion that magnets can lose their magnetism when placed in a strong magnetic field, dropped, or heated is difficult to comprehend.

♦ Relating magnetic force, which acts at a distance, to a push or pull, where contact is required, may cause difficulty.

♦ Labeling magnetic poles 'north' and 'south' is a little more unnatural to the first time learner than those familiar with magnetism may realize.

♦ Separating electricity and magnetism initially, then connecting them later (as with the electromagnet) may cause confusion if not handled carefully.

E.   LEARNING ABOUT MAGNETISM USING THE CONCEPTUAL CHANGE MODEL

TEACHING NOTES

Provide the following materials for each small group:

magnets(bar, cylindrical, horseshoe, disk)

paper clip	container of water
piece of wood	glass beaker or cup
rubber band	iron filings
aluminum foil	Styrofoam cup
iron nail	battery
piece of plastic	bell wire
common pin	

Remind students that magnets should not be placed on or near computers or computer diskettes, cassette tapes, or videotapes, or the information that is stored on them could be ruined.

ACTIVITY I: Magnetic or Nonmagnetic?

1. Commit to an Outcome

Suppose you are given a paper clip, a piece of wood, a rubber band, some aluminum foil, some plastic, an iron nail, and a penny. Predict which of these materials are will be attracted to a magnet and which ones will not . Give reasons for your predictions.

2. Expose Beliefs

In your group, share with others your beliefs about which of the materials are magnetic and which ones are not and your reasons for believing so. Have a representative from your group share the predictions and explanations of your group with the rest of the class.

3. Confront Beliefs

In your small group decide how you will test your ideas. Get the necessary materials and test your predictions. Based on your observations, what changes, if any, would you like to make in your reasoning?

4. Accommodate the Concept

What statement can you make about the type of materials that are magnetic and those that are not?

5. Extend the Concept

Using your ideas and those of others, go around the room, identify materials that you think are magnetic and non-magnetic, and then test them.

CAUTION: Keep all magnets away from computers, computer diskettes, cassette tapes, and videotapes or the information that is stored on them could be ruined.

6. Go Beyond

What other questions or activities would you like to pursue related to magnetic and non-magnetic materials ?

ACTIVITY II: Materials Through Which Magnetism Can Penetrate

1. Commit to an Outcome

For each of the following situations, predict whether or not the pin will be affected by the magnet. Give reasons for your predictions.

- a.   pin on top of a sheet of paper and magnet under the paper
- b.   pin on top of a stack of paper and magnet under the stack
- c.   pin on top of the desk and magnet under the desk
- d.   pin inside a glass beaker and magnet outside
- e.   pin inside a Styrofoam cup and magnet outside
- f.   pin inside a plastic container and magnet outside
- g.   pin in your hand and magnet under your hand
- h.   pin inside a plastic container that is floating in water and the magnet below the water (See Figure 1.)

pin in plastic box with box floating on water

two inches of water

Magnet underneath

Figure 1

2. Expose Beliefs

In your small group, share with others your predictions and the explanations as to whether the pin will be affected by the magnet in each situation. Have your representative share with everyone the predictions and the explanations of your group members.

3. Confront Beliefs

Get the necessary materials and test your predictions. Discuss your observations with others in your group.

4. Accommodate the Concept

Based on your observations and group discussion, what statement can you make about the nature of the materials that a magnet's effect can penetrate and those that it cannot? Share your statements with others.

5. Extend the Concept

What are some of the examples of the ability of a magnet's effects to penetrate materials with which you are familiar? Share your examples with others in your group.

Find other materials and test them to see if magnets' effects can penetratethem.

6. Go Beyond

What other questions and problems would you like to pursue about the ability of a magnet's effects to penetrate materials?

ACTIVITY III: Iron Filings and Magnets

1. Commit to an Outcome

If you sprinkled some iron filings on top of a sheet of paper, what shape would they take? What if you placed a magnet under the paper? Predict whether there will be a difference if you had

      a.   no magnet
      b.   a bar magnet
      c.   a horseshoe magnet
      d.   a disk magnet
      e.   a cylindrically shaped magnet

You may want to make drawings of what you think the pattern of the iron filings would look like and write down your reasons.

2. Expose Beliefs

Share your drawings and your reasons in your small group.

3. Confront Beliefs

Get the necessary materials and test your ideas. Did your ideas agree with your observations? Do you want to make any changes in your explanations?

4. Accommodate the Concept

Based on your observations and discussions, what statement can you make about the iron filing configurations you observed? What meaning can we attach to these observations?

5. Extend theConcept

What are some of the applications of what you observed here? Where have you seen examples of this phenomenon?

6. Go Beyond

What other questions and problems do you want to investigate related to the region around a magnet that you have observed here?

ACTIVITY IV: Strength of a Magnet

1. Commit to an Outcome

Of the four different magnets—a bar magnet, a horseshoe magnet, a disk magnet, and a cylindrical magnet—predict the order of their strength. Explain the reasons for your predictions.

2. Expose Beliefs

In your small group, share your predictions and explanations. Have a representative present the predictions and the explanations of each member to the class.

3. Confront Beliefs

In your group, decide on a way to test the strength of magnet. Get the necessary materials and use your method to test the strengths of different magnets. Compare your results with those of other groups.

4. Accommodate the Concept

Based on your observations and discussions, what statement can you make about the relationship between size, shape, and material of the magnet and its strength?

5. Extend the Concept

Share examples of magnets of different strengths. What do you think determines the strength of a permanent magnet?

6. Go Beyond

What questions, problems, or projects would you like to pursue about the strength of a permanent magnet?

ACTIVITY V: The Electromagnet

1. Commit to an Outcome

Wind several turns of bell wire around a steel nail. Connect the two bare ends of the wire to the two poles of a battery. (See Figure 2.) Predict what would happen if you brought the nail close to a heap of pins. Give reasons for your prediction.

coil of wire
around nail

battery   Figure 2

2. Expose Beliefs

Share in your small group your predictions and explanations. Again, have a representative share the predictions and the explanations of the members of your group with the rest of the class.

3. Confront Beliefs

Get the necessary materials and test your predictions and explanations. What revisions, if any, do you want to make in your explanations?

4. Accommodate the Concept

Based on your observations of the behavior of a coil of wire wound around a nail, what statements can you make? Share your statements with others in your group. What are the characteristics of an electromagnet? How is an electromagnet similar to or different from a permanent magnet?

5. Extend the Concept

Give examples of applications of electromagnets with which you are familiar. Design experiments to test the effects of the following on the strength of an electromagnet:

    a.   size of the nail
    b.   number of turns of wire
    c.   spacing between the turns of wire
    d.   number of batteries

Carry out the experiments. Describe a <u>strong</u> electromagnet.

6. Go Beyond

What other questions, problems, or projects do you want to pursue about electromagnets?

F.   REFERENCES

Finley, F. N. (1986). Evaluating instruction: the complementary use of clinical interviews. *Journal of Research in Science Teaching*. 23(7), 635-650.

Hapkiewicz, A. & Hapkiewicz, W. G. (1993). *Misconceptions in science*. Presented at the National Science Teachers Association regional meeting, Denver.

Project AIMS. (1991). *Mostly magnets*. Fresno, CA: AIMS Educational Foundation.

MENTAL MODEL BUILDING

A.   IDENTIFICATION OF THE CONCEPTS

models, construction of models, evaluation of models, and the use and importance of models

B.   BACKGROUND INFORMATION FOR THE TEACHER

How can students explore the meaning of models?

For quite a while in science education research, we have been talking about encouraging students to construct their own knowledge. Activities such as building scientific models, sharing models with classmates, and revising models fall naturally in the area of constructing knowledge.

Unlike the other units which deal with a particular science concept, this unit deals with the skill of building and refining scientific models. The activities will be different from the others covered in this book in two important ways: (1) Instead of beginning with a prediction about "what will happen," the student will be asked to construct a mental model; and (2) the students will evaluate their ideas by comparing their mental models to one another and to models from other sources and evaluating how well the models explain observable phenomena.

Often a model makes sense to the person who invented it and possibly others, but may have flaws and subtle inaccuracies that mislead children. In this unit, I propose that instead of forcing one teacher-selected model upon the student, students should have the opportunity to learn for themselves why models are needed and what role they play in various areas of science. With the use of imagination and careful observation, students can develop skill and confidence in their ability to construct their own models. The students also learn that they can question and judge the models proposed by scientists and others.

By drawing on students' ideas and the results of their discussions, you may ask the students to share their feelings and observations with regard to what they have done. Their activities and discussions can serve as an effective basis for the concept of *developing and refining mental models*. You may want to help the students to realize that in the study of science, we encounter various models of how things work. Scientists develop these models based on their own observations and imagination. Sometimes, models can be tested; e.g., open the pop machine, the toy, or the black box, and test the accuracy of the model(s) presented. But sometimes it is not so simple, or maybe even impossible, to directly compare a model with reality. In that case, a model is judged based on how well it explains the observable phenomenon.

It is important to develop the skill of constructing mental models and revising and refining those mental models based on observations and data. It is also important not to be afraid of questioning the models and ideas put forth by others. The history of science tells us that the models developed by scientists have been challenged and revised continuously (for example, the models of the structure of atoms).

Students will develop an understanding of the need for models and develop skills for refining models by building their own mental models. It is important to display all the models presented, so that students can compare different ways of explaining a particular phenomenon and assess the benefits and shortcomings of each. As they go through the activities, the concepts presented become more abstract. This sequence creates a progression toward more sophisticated models as the students gain confidence in simpler ones.

Note: For these activities, the students should be told that the items addressed cannot be opened, and the testing should consist of debating how well the various facets of the models explain what is being observed.

C. SOME KINDS OF MISCONCEPTIONS AND OTHER EFFECTS ON STUDENT LEARNING THAT RESULT FROM THE USE OF MODELS

♦ Even if they learn all of the terminology, students may sometimes incorrectly apply the experiences they have at the macroscopic level (things they can directly see and/or manipulate) to the microscopic level (things that are too small to experience directly).

♦ Students appear to learn (remember) the model and not the concept behind the model.

♦ Students erroneously attribute literal behavior of the model to the phenomena it is supposed to represent. For example, more students in one study believed that there was a higher likelihood of two planets colliding after the lesson than before because the model planets that were hung from the ceiling often bumped into one another when the wind blew.

D.   SOURCES OF STUDENTS' CONFUSION AND MISCONCEPTIONS

♦   Abstract models present difficulty for students who are still in the concrete operational stage (which often extends through high school).

♦   Textbooks use a tremendous variety of models for things like atoms. Particularly misleading are those that have physical properties of their own like marshmallows and toothpicks or nuts and bolts.

♦   Some textbooks shift in midstream between different symbols and representations used to convey abstract concepts such as molecules.

♦   The idea of what a model is, itself, is rarely presented for students to think about.

♦   Spatial ability has been shown to be related to success in abstract fields, and extending this conclusion to models seems feasible.

E.   LEARNING ABOUT MODELS USING THE CONCEPTUAL CHANGE MODEL

TEACHING NOTES

You will note that the initial stages of the conceptual change model have been modified for these activities. That is because students are asked to construct and explore mental models, rather than to predict the outcomes of experimental activities. At the end of the unit, you may ask your students to select another phenomenon or concept, build a mental model of how it works, and share it with other students in class.

The following materials will be necessary for the activities:

Black Box (per small group)
        (A Black Box is simply a sealed box with 1 or more items inside that slide
                or roll when the box is tilted or moved—geo blocks work well.)
a thin probe made of rigid wire or other material (as least as long as the box used)
baking soda and vinegar (teacher demonstration)
Styrofoam balls, marker, flashlight (or other materials requested by groups
        building moon phase models or models of the seasons)
Any available commercial models for demonstrating moon phases and seasons, chemical
        models, models of human anatomy, models of plants
Textbooks, posters, reference books that explain states of matter, seasons, and moon phases

ACTIVITY I. A Probing Box

1. Build Your Own Model(s)

What shape object do you think is inside the box? Lift, shake, and rotate the sealed box, or use the probe provided to probe inside the box, and write down or draw the shape of objects you think may be inside the box.

2. Expose Your Mental Model(s)

Share with the others in your group your drawings and thoughts about what is inside the black box. Give reasons for your ideas. As with other activities, have your representative present the models of individual members to the class .

3. Evaluate the Models Presented

In your group, vote on the model or models, including your own, which best describe what you hear and feel by moving the box. When you have decided, present the results of the group to the entire class. The whole class can then vote on which model or models best explain their observations.

4. Accommodate theConcept

Based on the sharing in your group and with the entire class, what is the role of a model? Who uses models? What makes a good model?

5. Extend the Concept

What are some examples of models with which you are familiar? Bring something to class, such as a mechanical toy, and challenge your teammates to build a mental model of how the object works.

ACTIVITY II. Inside a Soda (pop) Machine

1. Build Your Own Model

Get into your small groups, and reflect on your own experience with pop machines. (You put coins in and get a can of beverage and maybe some change.) Construct a mental model of how the machine works: what happens from the time you drop the coins in the slot to the time you receive the can and possibly the change?

2. Expose Mental Models

In your group, share your mental pictures of a how a pop machine works. You may do this by making sketches or discussing the models. The members in your small group need not agree completely about their models. From your group, select a representative to present the model or models of the group to the class.

3. Evaluate the Models Presented

After listening to all the views presented, the members of your group should debate the issue of which model(s) do a <u>better</u> job of explaining the inside of a pop machine. Base your decisions on *what you see or hear* from the time you drop the coin in the slot to the time the can comes out. Remember, you are trying to use your model to represent <u>what actually happens</u> inside the pop machine, so choose the models that work the best based on actual observations.

As a class, you may decide to vote on which models are "effective" or "defective" models of a pop machine.

ACTIVITY III. Day and Night

1. Build Your Own Model

Design a mental model for yourself about the occurrence of day and night. You may draw diagrams or use available materials to show your mental model. Provide reasons for the model you have constructed.

2. Expose Mental Models

Share in your group your individual models about the occurrence of day and night. Select a representative from your group to share with the class your group's ideas and models about what causes day and night.

3. Evaluate the Models Presented

Display the models proposed by individuals and those given in books and other materials. With these in mind, get in groups and use <u>your criteria</u> for an <u>effective</u> model and your own personal experiences to choose the models that best explain the occurrence of day and night.

4. Accommodate the Concept

Based on your discussions and your evaluation of the models, how would you explain what causes the occurrence of day and night? Which model and representation was most useful in helping you to make sense of this concept?

ACTIVITY IV. Phases of the Moon

1. Build Your Own Model

Using markers, flashlights, Styrofoam balls, or other materials, build your own model of how phases of the moon occur. Provide explanations for your mental model.

2. Expose Mental Models

Share your model and explanation with others in your group about what causes the phases of the moon. Have someone from your group present to the others in the class the models and explanations of the individuals in your group.

3. Evaluate the Models Presented

With all the models you can gather, including the models you made and those from text-books and commercial companies displayed, evaluate the <u>merits</u> and <u>effectiveness</u> of each model with your small group.

Spend time testing the models by making observations and collecting data for the next several weeks. Keep track of the phases of the moon and evaluate the proposed models on the basis of your own observations.

4. Accommodate the Concept

In your group, develop the concept of the phases of the moon. What explanations and models helped you to understand the phases of the moon? What statement can you make about the characteristics of an effective model?

ACTIVITY V. The Seasons

1. Build Your Own Model

You have experienced seasons of the year. Now you have an opportunity to build your own models about what causes seasons. Individually or in groups, use butcher paper, markers, balls, flashlights and other simple materials to build models about what you think causes the seasons.

2. Expose Mental Models

Share your models, your drawings, and physical models of what causes seasons first in your small groups, then with the entire group. After everyone has had the opportunity to share his or her ideas, you may wish to revise your own models, if necessary.

3. Evaluate the Models Presented

In your group, evaluate the models and the explanations proposed, including the models and the explanations by textbooks and commercially companies. In your group, list the most useful and least useful parts of each model. Select those models that are able to explain your observations the best.

4. Accommodate the Concept

As a class, develop the concept of the seasons using your own and your classmates' ideas, models, and explanations. Work toward producing a mental model of what causes the seasons. Which explanations or models helped you in understanding seasons? What are the characteristics of these more useful models or explanations?

5. Extend the Concept

Now that you have gone through building, sharing, and revising your models, think of other examples of models from other areas with which you are familiar. You may bring examples from any area of science, such as biology, geology, physics, and chemistry.

In your group discuss the following:

a. What are the criteria of effective models?
b. What are some examples of effective models and examples of models that are not effective?
c. Why do we need models?
d. How do we build models?
e. How do we test models?
f. How do we modify the models we have built?
g. What are the criteria for a "good" model?

6. Go Beyond

When out of class, think about these models and develop your own questions, concerns, and models about other topics you encounter to bring to class to share with others.

ACTIVITY VI. Ice Melts and Changes to Steam

1. Build Your Own Model

Consider the following demonstration. When an ice cube is placed in a beaker and slowly heated, you can observe the ice melting to liquid water, then changing to steam. (The water goes through changes in state of matter from solid to liquid to gas.) If you could see the smallest particle that makes up the ice, what mental picture do you imagine for what happens "inside" when ice changes to liquid water and finally to steam? You may choose to make drawings to better illustrate your point.

2. Expose Mental Models

Share in your group your models about what happens to the smallest particles when ice changes to liquid water and then to steam. In your presentations, use drawings or materials to illustrate what happens.

You may wish to make modifications in your view of what happens inside the material as it goes through the changes you see. Choose a representative from your group to present to the class the ideas and the models proposed by each member.

3. Evaluate the Models Presented

Display the models presented by individual members and models from textbooks and other developers of educational materials. In your small groups, consider all of these models and judge which ones make the most sense to you. Which of them can best explain some aspects of the observed changes as ice melts and is converted to steam? (You may choose more than one model as being especially effective.) Discuss how well each of the models presented by the individual members works in explaining what you see.

4. Accommodate the Concept

As a <u>class</u>, discuss the pros and cons of different models. Work toward developing <u>criteria</u> for <u>effective</u> models by evaluating the models and the ideas presented, including those from textbooks and instructional materials. Decide which ones best explain both your observations *and* what we know about the changes of states of matter. (Again, you may choose more than one model as being especially effective.)

When you have done this, discuss in your <u>small group</u> the criteria for an effective model based on such characteristics of matter as appearance, density, motion, and so on.

ACTIVITY VII. Combining Vinegar and Baking Soda

1. Build Your Own Model

Suppose you pour some vinegar into a beaker containing baking soda. Bubbles are produced, and heat is released.

Pouring a little vinegar on baking soda causes fizzing , releasing bubbles making a product totally different from the initial materials. After your teacher demonstrates this, build your own mental model of what happens when vinegar is poured on baking soda.

Get in your small groups and, based on past experience and what you have learned, construct a mental model of what happened. You can use drawings or simple materials to build a mental model of what happens when vinegar and baking soda come in contact.

2. Expose Mental Models

In your small group, share your mental models about what happens to vinegar and baking soda when they are added to each other. Appoint a representative from your group to present the models and the reasons for those models to the large group.

3. Evaluate the Models Presented

Consider the mental models presented by the individual members in your group, those presented by other groups, and those presented by textbooks and other instructional materials. In your group, evaluate the effectiveness of each of the models. Which model or models best explain the behavior of vinegar and baking soda and the product produced by mixing them?

4. Accommodate the Concept

Based on the discussions that occurred about the models presented, what are the characteristics of each model that are best able to explain the behavior of the smallest particle of the vinegar, baking soda, and product? What statement can you make about the models?

F.   REFERENCES

Dyche, S., McClurg, P.,.Stepans, J. I.; & Veath, M. L. (1993). Questions and conjectures concerning models, misconceptions and spatial ability. *School Science and Mathematics, 93(4),* 191-197.

Judson, H. F. (1980). *The search for solutions.* New York: Holt, Rinehart, and Winston.

Renner, J. W. & Marek, E. A. (1988). *The learning cycle and elementary school science teaching.* Portsmouth, New Hampshire: Heinemann Educational Books, Inc.

Stepans, J. I. & Veath, M. L. (Nov./Dec.1990). On research. *Science Scope, 33,* 52.

Stepans, J. I. & Veath, M. L. (May, 1994). How do students really explain changes in matter? *Science Scope, 17(8),* 31-35

Strauss, M. J. & Levine, S. H. (1985-86). Symbolism, science and developing minds. *Journal of College Science Teaching, 15(3),* 190-195.

HEAT

A.   IDENTIFICATION OF THE CONCEPTS

heat, temperature, the role of material in heat transfer, conduction, convection and radiation of heat

B.   BACKGROUND FOR THE TEACHER

What is heat?

Heat is the *total amount of internal energy*—energy from particle motion combined with any inter-particle energy—*contained in a particular volume* . We know, from common experience, that when two objects of different temperature are brought together, they eventually arrive at a common temperature. This is the result of a transfer of heat, which occurs faster with a greater difference in temperature of the systems. When we touch something cold with our warm hands, heat is transferred from our hands to the object because of the difference in the temperatures of the two systems. Heat is transferred in three ways : *conduction, convection and radiation*.

What is conduction?

Conduction is the process of *heat transfer without movement* of the matter itself. It occurs by *transfer of heat from one molecule to another*. An example of such transfer occurs in metal: if we place a metal spoon in a cup of hot chocolate, the part of the spoon that is outside the liquid is soon quite hot also. This is because of conduction.

What is convection?

Convection is the process of *heat transfer caused by the movement of gas or liquid*. Our cars use a fan to move heat away from the engine. This is one example of convection. Natural examples are also common. In weather systems, wind serves to transfer heat. In a pot of boiling water, hot water near the bottom of the pan swirls up and transfers heat to water farther from the stove burner.

What is radiation?

We receive energy from the sun through radiation. *Radiation* is the *transfer of energy through electromagnetic* waves. When radiation strikes an object that is not transparent, the energy of the wave is converted to heat energy. The air above the earth is transparent and, for the most part, is not heated by the radiant energy of the sun. Examples of heat transfer by radiation are heat felt from the sun and heat felt from "radiant" heaters.

What is temperature, and how is it different from heat?

Temperature is the description of the *average agitation or motion of the particles in a body or system*. It is related to the speed, and hence the kinetic energy, of particles. The temperature of a system provides information about the state of the system and helps in predicting the changes which will occur when the system comes in contact with other systems. Temperature is different from heat because it refers to an average quantity, not an amount of a quantity. For example, a cup and a bathtub may both have hot water of the same temperature in them, but the cup will cool much faster because it has less heat.

How do we measure heat and temperature?

We use calories to measure heat. One *calorie* is the amount of heat needed to raise the temperature of 1 gram of water of by 1 degree Celsius. A BTU (British Thermal Unit) is another unit used to measure heat. It is the English unit of heat and is equivalent to 252 calories.

Temperature is measured in either Celsius, Fahrenheit, or Kelvin. Scientists almost always use the Celsius or Kelvin scales because they have been designed to have a 100 degree separation between the boiling and freezing points of water. We are more familiar with the Fahrenheit scale, however, because it is used in all of our weather reports. The table below shows how the temperature scales correspond to one another.

Temperature Scale	Fahrenheit	Celsius	Kelvin *
Boiling Point of Water	212 degrees F	100 degrees C	373 K
Freezing Point of Water	32 degrees F	0 degrees C	273 K

* Note that units in Kelvin are not called "degrees."

What is a conductor or insulator of heat?

The reason we use metal pots and pans for cooking is that they are conductors of heat. *Conductors* transfer heat energy quickly and effectively. Copper is an excellent conductor, followed in effectiveness by aluminum, brass, and iron. Materials such as plastic and Styrofoam do not transfer heat efficiently. They are *insulators* of heat.

C. SOME REPRESENTATIVE STUDENT MISCONCEPTIONS ABOUT HEAT

◆ Heat makes things rise.

◆ Cold is opposite to heat.

◆ Heat acts as a fluid. It accumulates in one spot until that spot is full. Then that spot "bursts" and heat overflows to other parts of a substance (e.g, the metal rod in the activities below).

◆ Heat and cold are associated with air.

◆ Everything contains air bubbles, and some bubbles contain cold air and others hot air.

◆ Soft things melt more easily than hard things.

◆ The temperature of a body is related to its size and mass.

◆ Heat is a material substance like air or steam. It is made up of fumes that can transfer into and out of an object.

On the difference between heat and temperature:

◆ **Temperature is used to measure heat, and heat is "hot." (Actually temperature measures average particle motion, <u>not</u> the amount of heat. Also, some heat is present in everything, even things that feel cold.)**

◆ There is no difference between heat and temperature. Temperature is the amount of heat; it tells the hotness of something. More heat raises the temperature. (You can add more hot water to a bathtub of hot water, adding more heat without changing the temperature.)

◆ Heat is something that is started and maintained by a source.

◆ Heat moves around and rises.

◆ Heat is a substance which could be added to or removed from an object. For example, when a metal rod is heated, a substance from the flame enters the rod and then moves on.

◆ Larger ice cubes have a colder temperature.

◆ Metal is colder than plastic because cold passes through it more quickly than plastic.

◆ Metal is colder because it absorbs more cold than the plastic.

◆ The reason metals get hotter than other substances is because they can attract heat better than other substances.

◆ The color, thickness, and hardness of a material influence its ability to conduct heat.

D. SOURCES OF STUDENTS' CONFUSION AND MISCONCEPTIONS

◆ Everyday use of terms such as "heat" and "temperature" may contribute to students' confusion. The terms are often used in non-scientific contexts, such as "close the window so the heat does not escape" and "you must be sick, you have a temperature." In the first case, the implication is that heat is a material thing. The second case can seem to mean that heat and temperature are the same.

◆ Physical surroundings and the sensation of hot and cold play important roles in children's conceptions about phenomena associated with heat. For example, the direction of conduction of heat in relation to the human body influences thinking. A copper bowl and a plastic bowl may share the same temperature, but the copper one will feel colder because it conducts heat away from the fingers more quickly. It is difficult for students to think of conduction when they FEEL a sensation of cold.

◆ Instruction on the subject, including the introduction of kinetic theory, has had little effect on students' understanding of heat because it is abstract and does not clearly contradict their experiential framework.

◆ Many of the phenomena associated with heat and temperature are counter-intuitive.

◆ In everyday language, we imply that objects either possess heat or do not possess heat (i.e., "are cold"). From the perspective of scientists, all everyday objects have some heat and the potential to transfer energy to another object of lower temperature.

E. LEARNING ABOUT HEAT USING THE CONCEPTUAL CHANGE MODEL

TEACHING NOTES

The following materials will be needed for the activities in this chapter. If possible, provide a set of materials for each small group.

> copper rods of same length, different circumferences*
> aluminum rod*
> iron rod*
> candles, matches
> wax (paraffin, old candles, crayon)
> length of thin, flexible wire
> beaker
> 4 identical bottles or jars
> dropper
> ink or dye
> string
> index card

*These rods can be ordered from most science equipment companies.

(Organizing sets of materials in plastic bins or shoe boxes will aid in management of student movement during activities utilizing lighted candles.)

Safety should be discussed with students before the distribution of matches. Be sure students keep clothing and long hair pulled back out of the way of burning candles.

ACTIVITY I: Heat Conduction

A. Melting wax on a copper rod

1. Commit to an Outcome

Predict what would happen to wax placed at spots along a copper rod if the rod is heated at the other end with a candle (Figure 1). Give reasons for your predictions.

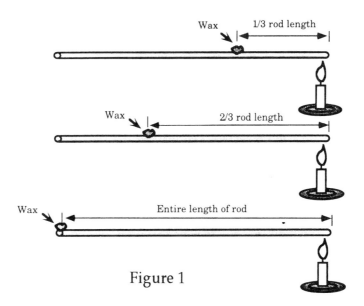

Figure 1

2. Expose Beliefs

Share with others in your small group your predictions about what will happen to the wax and your reasons for those predictions. Have a representative from your group share the predictions and the explanations of your small group with others in the class.

3. Confront Beliefs

With your group, get the tray containing the rod, candle, wax, and matches. Test your predictions and make revisions in your explanations, if necessary. **Keep clothing and hair out of the way of the burning candle.**

4. Accommodate the Concept

Based on your observations and discussions, what statement can you make about the behavior of heat when a copper rod is heated?

B. Melting wax on rods of different thickness

1. Commit to an Outcome

Predict what would happen if you used several different rod sizes and repeated Activity IA. Write down your predictions and explanations. (See Figure 2.)

Figure 2

2. Expose Beliefs

Share your predictions and explanations with others in your group. Again, have a representative from your group share these predictions with the class.

3. Confront Beliefs

Test your predictions and explanations by getting the additional rods and testing them with help from your group. **Again, be cautious while burning the candle.**

4. Accommodate the Concept

Based on your observations and discussions with the group, what statement can you make about the effect of the thickness of the rod on the conduction of heat in rods?

C. Melting wax on rods of different metals

1. Commit to an Outcome

Suppose we have rods of the same size and shape made of several different metals—aluminum, copper, and iron—and place wax at one end. Predict whether there would be a difference in the time it would take to melt the wax on the different rods if we heated the opposite end of each rod. Give reasons for your predictions.

2. Expose Beliefs

Share your predictions and explanations with others in your group. Appoint a member of your group to share the predictions and explanations of the group with the rest of the class.

3. Confront Beliefs

With the other members of your group, get the necessary materials and test your ideas. **Be careful with the burning candle.**

4. Accommodate the Concept

After testing your predictions, make a statement related to the role of the various rod materials in heat conduction.

5. Extend the Concept

What are some of the examples with which you are familiar related to Activities IA, IB, and IC? How do we use the concept of heat conduction in our daily lives?

Apply what you have learned in IA, IB, and IC to try to predict what would happen if you made a coil from a wire and lowered it around a candle flame (as in Figure 3). Share your predictions and test them. **Be careful not to burn yourself on the candle flame.**

Figure 3

6. Going Beyond

What are some of the questions and problems related to the conduction of heat that you would like to pursue?

ACTIVITY II: Heat Convection

A. The paper snake

1. Commit to an Outcome

We have available a coil made from a strip of paper, hanging with a string. Predict what would happen if we suspend it above a lit candle (as in Figure 4). Give reasons for your predictions.

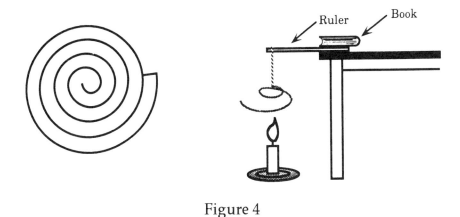

Figure 4

2. Expose Beliefs

Share your predictions and explanations with other members of your group. Have one member from your group present the predictions and the explanations of the group to the class.

3. Confront Beliefs

Get the necessary materials and test your predictions on the effect of a burning candle on a suspended paper snake. **(Be careful not to catch the paper snake on fire.)** Based on your observations, make appropriate revisions in your explanations.

4. Accommodate the Concept

Make a statement explaining the result of your observations and discussions.

B. Hot water and ink

1. Commit to an Outcome

A beaker filled with water sits at the edge of a table, as in Figure 5. Suppose that you use a dropper to gently place a drop of ink or food coloring at the bottom of the beaker at the place that is hanging over the table (while trying to disturb the water as little as possible). Predict what would happen if you began to heat this part of the beaker with a lit candle. Give reasons for your prediction.

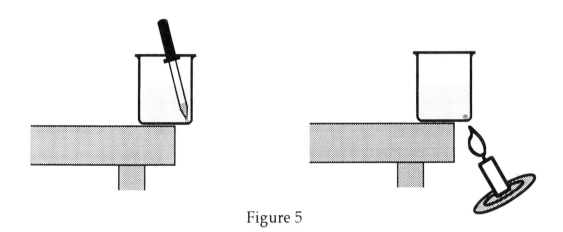

Figure 5

2. Expose Beliefs

Share your predictions and explanations with others in your group. Again, have a representative from your group present the predictions and the explanations of the group to the class.

3. Confront Beliefs

Get the necessary materials and test your predictions. Based on the results of your observations do you want to make any changes in your explanations?

4. Accommodate the Concept

Make a statement explaining your observations about what happened to the ink or food coloring inside the beaker as it was being heated.

C. Hot and cold bottles of water

1. Commit to an Outcome

Suppose we have four identical bottles, and we do the following: fill two bottles with cold water, and the other two bottles with hot water. Then we mix food coloring with one of the bottles of cold water and with one of the bottles of hot water. We place an index card over the top of each bottle that now contains colored water. (Figure 6a.)

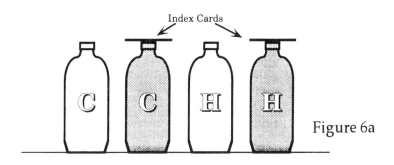

Figure 6a

Predict what will happen if we take the two bottles with food coloring (which are "sealed" with index cards) and place them upside-down over the other two bottles. This will be done so that the colored hot water is placed over the plain cold water and the colored cold water is placed over the plain hot water. (See Figure 6b.) What do you think will happen if the index cards are removed when the bottle openings are aligned? Give reasons for your predictions.

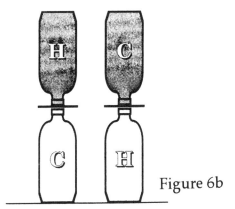

Figure 6b

2. Expose Beliefs

Share your predictions and explanations with the other members of your group. Have a group representative present the predictions and explanations of the group to the class.

3. Confront Beliefs

Get the necessary materials and test your predictions. Make revisions in your explanations, if necessary.

4. Accommodate the Concept

Using observations from Activities IIA, IIB, and IIC, what statements can you make about the role of heat in the behavior of air and water?

5. Extend the Concept

What examples can you give illustrating the behavior of heat that you have observed here?

6. Go Beyond

What questions and problems would you like to pursue on the behavior of heat in gases and liquids?

F. REFERENCES

Albert, E. (1978). Development of the concept of heat in children. *Science Education, 62(3),* 389-399.

Clough, E. E. & Driver, R. (1985). Secondary students' conceptions of the conduction of heat: bringing together scientific and personal views. *Physics Education, 20,* 176-182.

Erickson, G.L. (1979). Children's conceptions of heat and temperature. *Science Education, 63(2),* 221-230.

Erickson, G. L. (1980). Children's viewpoints of heat: a second look. *Science Education, 64(3),* 323-336.

Erickson, G. L. & Tiberghien, A. (1985). Heat and temperature. In *Children's ideas in science.* R. Driver, E. Guesne, and A. Tiberghien (Eds). Philadelphia: Open University Press.

Friedl, A. (1991). *Teaching science to children.* New York: McGraw-Hill.

Heating and cooling. (1971). Elementary science study. New York: McGraw-Hill

Liem, T. (1987). *Invitation to science inquiry.* Lexington , MA: Ginn Press.

Rogan, J. M. (1988). Development of a conceptual framework of heat. *Science Education, 72(1),* 103-113.

Shayer, M. & Wylam, H. (1981). The development of the concepts of heat and temperature in 10-13 year-olds. *Journal of Research in Science Teaching, 18(5),* 419-434.

WAVES

A.   IDENTIFICATION OF THE CONCEPTS

waves, conceptual importance of waves, definition of a wave, characteristics of waves, water waves, waves in springs, waves in strings, superposition of waves, behavior of waves (reflection, refraction, interference, and diffraction), transverse and longitudinal waves, and standing waves

B.   BACKGROUND INFORMATION FOR THE TEACHER

What is a wave?

What do sound, water, string, springs, and light have in common? They can all be associated with waves. When we drop a stone in water, waves are produced. Vibrating one end of string produces waves, and spring motion is wave motion. Sound is a wave, manifesting itself in the form of pressure vibrations. Light also has wave properties. Simply put, *waves are the mechanism of vibrations (and energy) being transported from one point to another*.

Why is the concept of waves important?

Waves and properties of waves not only explain the movement of water, vibrations of strings and springs, propagation of sound, and behavior of light, but also many other behaviors in nature ranging from subatomic particles to the universe.

How can we define a wave?

To totally define a wave, we need to speak about *frequency* (the number of vibrations or oscillations in a given time), *amplitude* (displacement from the rest position), *period* (time for one complete oscillation), and *wavelength* (distance between successive similar points). (See Figure I.)

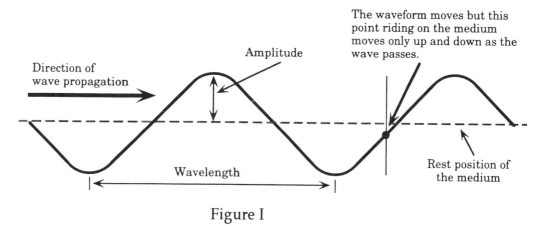

Figure I

What are the characteristics of a wave?

a.   When an incoming wave strikes something, it is *reflected*. We can see this when water waves hit a barrier. When we hear an echo, it is the result of reflection of sound. Seeing ourselves in a mirror is the result of reflection of light. Finally, when vibrations in a string return, this is another example of wave *reflection*.

b.   When light goes from air into water, it slows down. When water waves travel from a shallow area into a deep area, they change speed. These are examples of the *refraction* property of waves.

c.   When two beams of coherent light (such as different colors of laser light) meet they produce a new result. When water waves produced by two sources meet, they give rise to a new wave pattern, different from the two initial waves. When two or more sound waves meet, they produce a new sound or noise. These are examples of the *interference* of waves.

d.   When waves pass through an opening, they spread. The pattern produced depends on the wavelength of the incoming wave and the size of the opening, so several distinct patterns are possible. This phenomenon, known as *diffraction*, is demonstrated when light, sound, or water waves go around corners. Since light waves are very small, a very small opening is needed to see their diffraction. Sound diffraction occurs all the time, since many everyday objects cause it, so we rarely notice it, but with water, we get a clear picture of diffraction. (See Figure II.)

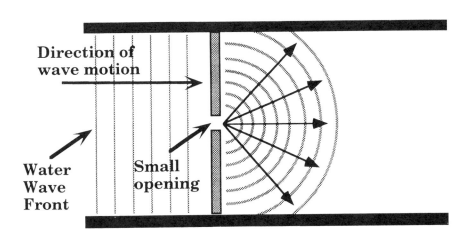

Figure II

What are the types of waves?

A piece of paper taped to a vibrating string will have an up-and-down motion; i.e., perpendicular to the direction of wave motion. This is an illustration of a *transverse* wave, as in Figure III a.

A spring, when set in motion by squeezing one part together and letting go, will vibrate in the same direction as the direction of travel of the vibration. This type of wave is called a *longitudinal* wave, as in Figure III b. Sound waves are longitudinal waves.

Figure IIIa — TRANSVERSE WAVE

type of waves on a string where string motion is perpendicular to direction of wave travel.

Figure IIIb — LONGITUDINAL WAVE

Above, we use springs as an example of a longitudinal wave, but springs can also transmit transverse waves, like a string would. We say springs exhibit both transverse and longitudinal waves. In this way, they are like the earth in an earthquake, when it also exhibits both kinds of wave motion.

What is wave superposition?

If two waves meet in the same medium, they will each proceed without regard to each other, including passing through each other. But while they overlap, the amplitude of the combined wave will be the total of the two amplitudes added together at each place where they overlap, as in Figure IV. This principle underlies other overall wave phenomena, such as interference.

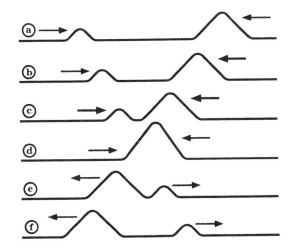

Figure IV

What are standing waves?

Sometimes incoming and reflected vibrations meet and actually interfere additively. They are superimposed and produce *standing waves*, as in Figure V. Looking at this occurrence, we see no apparent motion of the wave. Think of a jump rope, creating a "double" standing wave because of vibrations both up and down and left and right. While the rope moves, the location of the wave does not. This is why they are called standing waves.

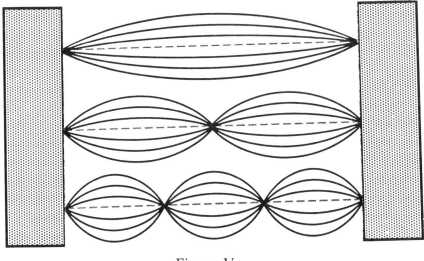

Figure V

C. SOME REPRESENTATIVE STUDENT MISCONCEPTIONS ABOUT WAVES

♦ Students often think of frequency in terms of <u>time</u> units and confuse it with <u>period</u>.

♦ The motion of the medium, up and down for water waves, is frequently confused with the motion of the wave itself, outward from a pebble dropped in a calm pool.

♦ Students often confuse the independent aspects of waves—primarily amplitude, frequency, and velocity—into just two parts, the motion of the medium and the overall intensity. For example, a common belief is that a rapid oscillation ensures a large amplitude and fast velocity. Or, conversely, a small amplitude implies a slow velocity.

♦ Wave collisions, according to the intuition of many students, result in the permanent cancellation of both waves, as if they were mechanical objects.

D. SOURCES OF STUDENTS' CONFUSION AND MISCONCEPTIONS

♦   The relationship between frequency and period requires an understanding of ratios, which is a difficult concept for many students.

♦   It is possible to acquire and use all of the wave vocabulary without gaining much understanding of waves themselves. Often, use of the words is essentially all that is tested.

♦   Wave motion is a cumulative phenomenon of much local motion. The distinction between the two is a subtle one, but one that is crucial for understanding.

E. LEARNING ABOUT WAVES USING THE CONCEPTUAL CHANGE MODEL

TEACHING NOTES

Provide the following materials for each small group if possible:
> length of string or rope
> Slinky spring
> clear glass or plastic pan (glass cake pan or plastic shoe box)
> flashlight
> ruler
> dropper
> water
> heavy cardboard or flexible plastic to form non-straight barriers (Activity II C)
> thick glass plate or block of paraffin to create shallow area in water

To create the shallow/deep water needed for Activity II A, have students put about 1 inch of water into the clear pan, then place the thick glass plate at one end.

It will be much easier to see the results of Activity II C if students suspend the flashlight directly over the pan of water in a fixed position. The light moves too much if someone holds the flashlight. Be sure the students have the water pan raised on books or other supports.

ACTIVITY I: Wave Behavior

A. <u>Wave patterns</u>

1. Commit to an Outcome

Predict the pattern produced for each of the following:

      a. a string tied at one end, set in motion by vibrations from your hand
      b. a Slinky spring on a flat surface set in motion by squeezing coils to one fixed end
      c. a drop of water dropped in a pan of water.

Illustrate your ideas with drawings and give reasons for your predictions.

2. Expose Beliefs

In your group, share your predictions, drawings, and reasons. A representative from your group will share the predictions of your group members about the behavior of string, a Slinky, and water with the whole class.

3. Confront Beliefs

With other members of the group, get a rope, a Slinky, and a pan of water and test your predictions. Revise your explanations, if necessary. What did you observe? Did your observations agree with your predictions?

4. Accommodate the Concept

Based on what you have observed, what statements can you make about the behavior of a string set in motion, a Slinky set in motion, and a stone dropped in a pan of water? What similarities do you see in the three different motions?

5. Extend the Concept

What other examples of these kinds of motion are you familiar with? Share your experiences with waves with others in your group.

B. Wave reflections

1. Commit to an Outcome

For the three situations in Activity IA (the string, the Slinky, and the water wave), predict what would happen if the vibration (wave) struck a barrier? This time, we will use a ruler to make a straight water wave. For the string and the Slinky, tying one end firmly to a fixed object would make a barrier. For the water wave, placing a straight object in the path of the wave would make a barrier. (See Figure 1.) Make drawings and give reasons for your predictions.

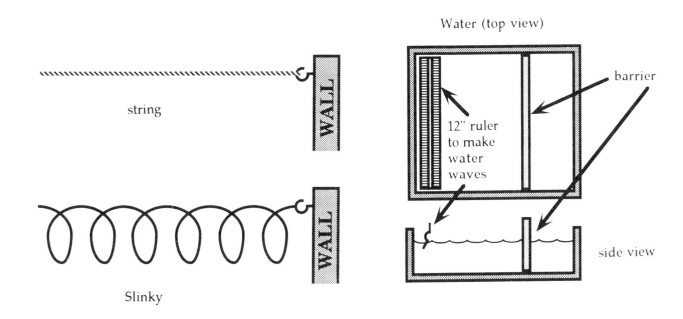

Figure 1

2. Expose Beliefs

Share your predictions and drawings for what you think will happen when waves in strings, water, and in Slinky springs strike barriers. Have someone from your group share with the class the predictions and reasons about the behavior of waves striking a barrier.

3. Confront Beliefs

Test your ideas by observing the behavior of each kind of wave hitting a barrier. What did you observe? Were there any surprises? Did the observations agree with your predictions? What changes do you want to make in your thinking, based on what you have seen?

4. Accommodate the Concept

What statements can you make, using drawings if necessary, about waves striking barriers? Share your statements with others in your group.

5. Extend the Concept

What would happen if you used different barrier shapes (see Figure 2 for some examples) in the pan of water and observed the behavior of water waves?

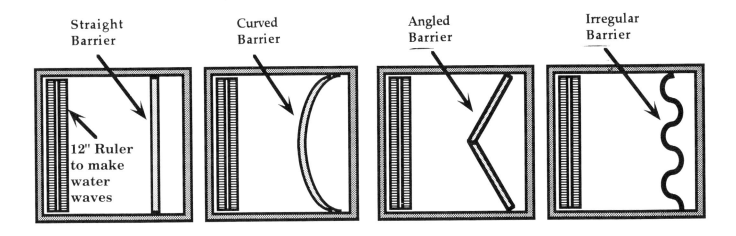

Figure 2

C. Water waves produced by two sources

1. Commit to an Outcome

Predict what patterns will be produced in the pan of water if two drops of water are dropped at the same time in the pan of water. Make drawings showing your predictions and give reasons for your predictions.

2. Expose Beliefs

Share with others in your group your predictions and drawings and your reasons for the patterns developed by two drops in a pan of water. Have someone from your group share the predictions and drawings of the members with the class.

3. Confront Beliefs

Get a clear plastic pan of water, raise it from the table, place a large sheet of plain white paper under it, and a light above it. (This way, you can see the wave patterns clearly on the sheet of paper.) Test your beliefs by using a dropper and releasing water droplets. Observe the patterns that result. You may need to try this more than once to see the result clearly.

What did you observe? Did the observations agree with your predictions?

4. Accommodate the Concept

Based on what you have observed and discussed, what statements can you make about the patterns produced when water waves meet each other? Share your statements with others.

5. Extend the Concept

What patterns are produced when the incoming waves and reflected waves meet? Using the rope, take note of this. What do you observe?

How would you apply the behavior of water waves to
     a. sound waves?
     b. light?

Give examples and think of ways that one could demonstrate them.

6. Go Beyond

Think of additional questions, problems, and projects you would like to pursue on waves meeting one another.

ACTIVITY II: Further Wave Properties

A. Water moving from a deep to a shallow area

1. Commit to an Outcome

Predict whether a straight wave pattern, again made with a ruler, would change if water waves traveled from a deep area to a shallow area. (See Figure 3.) Give reasons for your beliefs and make drawings showing your predictions.

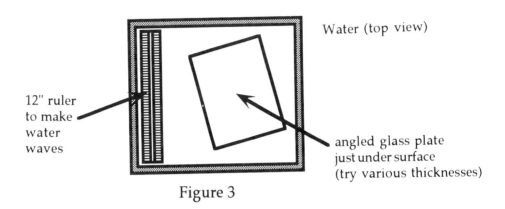

Water (top view)

12" ruler to make water waves

angled glass plate just under surface (try various thicknesses)

Figure 3

2. Expose Beliefs

Share your drawings, predictions, and reasons about what you think will happen if water waves move from an area of deep water to a shallow area. Have someone from your group share with the class the drawings, predictions, and explanations of the members.

3. Confront Beliefs

Get the pan of water and place a glass plate or paraffin in the bottom to make different depths of water. Using the ruler, make some water waves and observe the patterns as waves move from a deep area to a shallow area. What did you observe? Did your observations agree with your predictions? What changes do you want to make in your thinking?

4. Accommodate the Concept

Based on what you have observed and your discussions, what statement can you make about what happens when water waves move from a deep to a shallow area?

5. Extend the Concept

How can you apply what has been observed here to other waves such as sound, light, and waves in strings? What would you do to test your ideas?

B. <u>Waves going around corners</u>

1. Commit to an Outcome

Suppose we placed a barrier that extended about halfway across the pan of water (as shown in Figure 4). If we make a water wave, predict what will happen to the wave patterns as they pass the edges of the barrier. Make drawings and give reasons for your thoughts.

Water (top view)

Barrier (half way across)

12" ruler to make water waves

Figure 4

side view

2. Expose Beliefs

Share with others in your group your predictions, drawings and reasons for your predictions.

3. Confront Beliefs

Using the water pan with the barrier in place, make a water wave with the ruler and test your ideas about what happens to water waves going near the edges of a barrier. What did you observe? Did your observations agree with your predictions?

4. Accommodate the Concept

What statement can you make about the ability of waves to go around corners?

5. Extend the Concept

What would happen to the water waves if a barrier with several small openings were placed in the water? Make predictions and test them.

What are some examples of this phenomenon? What are the applications of this to the behavior of
     a. light?
     b. sound?

6. Go Beyond

Think of additional questions, problems, and projects you would like to pursue related to the wave phenomena discussed here.

F. REFERENCES

Freeman, I. (1965). *Physics made simple*. New York: Doubleday & Co.

Geddis, A. (April, 1990). *What to do about "misconceptions"—a paradigm shift*. Paper presented at the annual meeting of the American Educational Research Association, Chicago, Illinois. ERIC document 351186.

Scott, D. (1986). *The physics of vibrations and waves*. Ohio: Merrill Publishing Co.

Snir, J. (1989). Making waves: a simulation and modeling computer-tool for studying wave phenomena. *Journal of Computers in Mathematics and Science Teaching, 8(4)*, 48-53.

SOUND

A. IDENTIFICATION OF THE CONCEPTS

sound, sound waves, speed of sound, music, musical instruments

B. BACKGROUND INFORMATION FOR THE TEACHER

<u>What is sound?</u>

Sound is form of energy caused by back-and-forth vibrations. We hear sounds with our ears, but our ears work by sensing vibrations. We can detect vibrations directly by putting our hand on our Adam's apple when we speak, touching a ringing bell, or touching a ringing tuning fork to the surface of water.

<u>How does sound travel?</u>

Unlike light, sound travels at a speed slow enough for us to notice a delay between when a sound is produced and heard. This is why we notice a delay after we see a lightning strike before we hear thunder.

Sound can only travel through a material or *medium*—it cannot travel through empty space. Air is the medium with which we are most familiar. This is why we can hear sounds that originate somewhere away from us. We can also put our ears on a table top and hear sounds transmitted through the wood. In fact, we can hear two different sounds coming from the same source, one transmitted through air and one through wood. Many years ago, Plains Indians used to put their ears to the ground to detect the movement of a buffalo herd or riders on horseback. This further illustrates that sound can travel in various media. It travels better and faster in some media than others.

<u>What factors determine the speed of sound?</u>

Sound travels faster in media which are more elastic or more dense. Another factor that affects the speed of sound is temperature. The higher the temperature of the medium, the higher the speed of sound in that medium. Following are some sample speeds of sound in various media at room temperature:

Material (medium)	Speeed of Sound (m/s)
air	344
water	1460
wood	3350
iron	5030

What are the characteristics of sound?

Unlike light or water, sound travels in longitudinal waves. Since sound is a wave, it has the properties of wave—frequency, wavelength, and amplitude. It also reflects, refracts, and interferes like any other wave. *Frequency* , by definition, is the number of vibrations per second, but we <u>hear</u> differences in frequency as differences in <u>pitch</u>. *Wavelength* is the distance between two consecutive wave compressions. *Amplitude* is related to the loudness of sound. *Echoes* are an example of sound *reflection*. The *refraction* property of sound is responsible for sound changing speed as it goes from one medium to another. *Interference* is the mixing of two or more sounds, resulting in a new sound.

What is the difference between noise and music?

A musical note is a sound wave of a particular frequency. When we combine notes that have frequencies of small integer ratios, such as 3:2, 4:3, etc, we hear the pleasing combinations that are commonly used in music. Noise, on the other hand, is a random mixture of all frequencies without any discernible form or pattern.

What is resonance?

If we blow across the top of a bottle or hold a ringing tuning fork above a tube, we will vibrate a column of air. Certain air column heights produce very effective sound, because the air column vibrates naturally at the same frequency as the sound. (This natural frequency can be understood using the analogy of a park swing. While we can kick our feet back and forth however we want, there is one frequency that works particularly well at getting the swing to move.) When we vibrate something at its natural frequency, this is *resonance*.

Similarly, vibrating objects such as guitar strings and air columns in a flute have a resonance frequency of their own. We can change these resonance frequencies by changing the length of the guitar string or by changing the amount of closed-in air in a flute with our fingers. (This would be analogous to shortening the chain on the swing.)

C.   SOME REPRESENTATIVE STUDENT MISCONCEPTIONS ABOUT SOUND

♦   Sound cannot travel through solids and liquids.

♦   Sound can travel through a vacuum, such as space.

♦   Sound can be produced without using any materials.

♦   Hitting an object harder changes the pitch of the sound produced.

D. SOURCES OF STUDENTS' CONFUSION AND MISCONCEPTIONS

♦ As teachers, we speak of sound vibrations from sources as diverse as tuning forks, vocal cords, tapping, and blowing into bottles. Unless care is taken to connect these diverse methods of generating sound to common principles, confusion of young students will likely result.

♦ Connecting the concept of sound to waves may cause confusion, since sound waves are not observable like water waves, for example.

♦ Textbooks state that sound needs a medium in which to travel. While there is no trouble thinking of wood or water as a medium, air is not tangible in the same way. To make sense of this, students need to comprehend that air is substantive matter.

♦ Sound as a form of mechanical energy is difficult for many students to accept.

♦ Many of the concepts associated with sound require formal constructions, which are beyond the capability of a large number of students.

♦ The notions of sound travel and sound detection are intrinsically abstract, and difficult for many students.

E. LEARNING ABOUT SOUND USING THE CONCEPTUAL CHANGE MODEL

TEACHING NOTES

Provide the following materials for each small group:

four identical glass bottles
tuning fork
plastic straws
metal spoon
5 thin glass goblets or drinking glasses
string
nylon filament (fishing line)
thin wire
rubber bands of various sizes and thicknesses
cylinder open at both ends

ACTIVITY I: Heights of Air Columns

A. Blowing on an air column

1. Commit to an Outcome

Suppose you have four bottles. One is empty, one is 1/4 full of water, one is about 2/3 full of water, and one is nearly full. (See Figure 1.) Predict what difference, if any, there will be if you blow across the top of each bottle. Give reasons for your predictions.

Figure 1

2. Expose Beliefs

Share your predictions about the results of blowing across the bottles. Write your ideas on the newsprint or butcher paper provided. Have a representative from your group share the predictions and explanations of all members of your group with the large group.

3. Confront Beliefs

Have one member of your group bring the tray of bottles, so everyone in the group has the opportunity to test predictions and revise their explanations.

4. Accommodate the Concept

Again, have a representative from your group present the observations of your group to the class. Based on the observations and discussion, what statement can you make about the relationship between the column of air in the bottle and the sound generated?

B. Tuning fork and an air column

1. Commit to an Outcome

If we held a vibrating tuning fork above a cylinder with both ends open (as in Figure 2), predict how the sound would change as we lowered the cylinder into a container of water (changing the length of the air column).

Hollow glass tube open on each end

Glass tube lowered into water

Figure 2

2. Expose Beliefs

Share your predictions and explanations on the effect of the length of air column of the sound generated with your small group. Choose a representative to present the predictions and explanations of group members to the entire class.

3. Confront Beliefs

Test your ideas by working with the materials. Observe the effect of changing the air column on the sound generated by the tuning fork.

C. Straws

1. Commit to an Outcome

Suppose you have a plastic drinking straw, with one end flattened and cut in a triangular shape. (See Figure 3.)

Soda straw

Figure 3

Predict how the sound would change if, as you are blowing through the straw, you cut small pieces off the other end of the straw. Give reasons for your predictions.

2. Expose Beliefs

Share your predictions and explanations about what will happen with your group. Then, have your representative share the predictions and explanations of the group with the class.

3. Confront Beliefs

Get a few straws and a pair of scissors and test your predictions. Revise your explanations, if necessary.

4. Accommodate the Concept

Based on your observations and the discussion in activities A, B, and C, what statement can be made about the effect of air column height (length) on the sound produced?

Can you predict the particular heights of air columns that will produce the BEST effect? In your small group test your ideas with the cylinder and the container of water. What is significant about the particular heights that produce the best effect?

5. Extend the Concept

What are some of the examples of the relationship between height (length) of the air column and the sound produced? If you play a musical instrument, you may want to bring it and demonstrate the use of the principle.

6. Go Beyond

What additional questions and problems would you want to pose for investigation on the effect of the height of air column and the type of sound?

ACTIVITY II. Tapping the Bottles

1. Commit to an Outcome

In Activity A, what difference do you think you would notice in sounds if, instead of blowing across the bottles, you were to tap the bottles with a metal spoon? Give reasons for your predictions.

2. Expose Beliefs

Share ideas in your small group, then have your group representative share with the class the predictions and explanations of each individual group member.

3. Confront Beliefs

Test your ideas by working with bottles containing different amounts of water and a metal spoon.

4. Accommodate the Concept

Based on your observations and discussions in your small group and the entire class, what statements can you make about the relationship between the sounds produced and the mass of an object? What is the difference in the sounds produced between blowing across bottles and tapping them ?

5. Extend the Concept

What are some of the examples related to this concept with which you are familiar?

6. Go Beyond

Can you think of additional questions and problems about this phenomenon that you may want to investigate?

ACTIVITY III. Glass Goblets

1. Commit to an Outcome

Suppose you have five thin drinking glasses or goblets. One glass is empty, one is 1/4 filled with water, one is 1/2 filled, one is 2/3 filled, and one is filled to the rim. Predict what will happen if you rub the rims of each each glass with a moistened finger. Predict what will happen if you gently tap the side of each goblet or glass with a small metal spoon? Will there be a difference in the sounds produced? If so, how?

2. Expose Beliefs

Share your predictions and explanations with members of your group, then have your group representative present the predictions and explanations of the members of your group to the class.

3. Confront Beliefs

Get the five goblets or glasses, water, and a spoon. Test your ideas.

4. Accommodate the Concept

Based on observations you made by rubbing the rims and by tapping the sides of the goblets, what statement can you make about the relationship between the sound that is produced and the amount of air and water you are vibrating?

5. Extend the Concept

Can you give examples of where you have seen this phenomenon?

6. Go Beyond

What additional questions or problems would you want to pose for the investigation of the glass goblets?

ACTIVITY IV. A Spoon Tied to a String, Nylon, and Wire

1. Commit to an Outcome

Predict what sound you will hear if you tie the middle of a string to a metal spoon, touch the ends of the string to your ears, and tap the spoon on the edge of the table. Explain your predictions. Also, predict if there will be a difference in the sound if instead of cotton string you used (a) nylon filament and (b) wire. Give reasons for your predictions.

2. Expose Beliefs

Share your predictions and explanations with the others in your group. Take part as others in class present their predictions and explanations.

3. Confront Beliefs

Acquire a spoon, some string, nylon filament, and wire. Test your predictions. If necessary, make changes in your explanations.

4. Accommodate the Concept

Based on the observations you made on sounds resulting from tapping a spoon connected to string, wire, and nylon, what statements can you make?

5. Extend the Concept

Can you give examples of where you have seen this phenomenon in your daily life? Are you familiar with any musical instruments that make use of this principle? Would there be a difference in sound if you tied empty cups to the ends of the string and held the cups against your ears? Why do you think so?

6. Go Beyond

What additional questions or problems would you like to pursue related to tapping objects?

ACTIVITY V. Sound Generated by a Tuning Fork Through Air, Wood, Glass, and Metal

1. Commit to an Outcome

Predict the difference, if any, in the sound generated by a ringing tuning fork as it passes through (a) air, (b) wood, (c) glass, and (d) metal. Explain the reasons for your predictions.

2. Expose Beliefs

Share your predictions and explanations about the sound generated by a tuning fork passing through air, wood, glass and metal with members of your group. Have a member of your group share the predictions and explanations with the entire class.

3. Confront Beliefs

Test your predictions and explanations by listening to the sounds generated by a ringing tuning fork through air, glass, wood, and metal.

4. Accommodate the Concept

Based on your observations and discussions, what statement can you make about the passage of sound generated by ringing a tuning fork through air, glass, wood, and metal?

5. Extend the Concept

Try to cite examples of this phenomenon.

6. Go Beyond

What additional questions or problems would you want to pursue related to a tuning fork transferring vibrations through different materials?

ACTIVITY VI. Rubber Band Sounds

1. Commit to an Outcome

Predict the difference, if any, in the sounds that will be produced by plucking a rubber band if we change the (a) length, (b) tension, and (c) thickness of the rubber band.

2. Expose Beliefs

Share your predictions and explanations about the effects, if any, of length, tension, and thickness of a rubber band on the sounds generated by plucking it.

3. Confront Beliefs

Get the necessary materials and test your predictions. Make revisions in your explanations, if necessary, related to the effects of length, tension and thickness of a rubber band on the sound generated by plucking it.

4. Accommodate the Concept

Based your observations and discussions, what statement can you make about the effect of length, tension, and thickness of a rubber band on the sound generated by plucking it?

5. Extend the Concept

Relate the concept to examples from your own experience.

6. Go Beyond

Try thinking of related questions and problems you would like to pursue.

F.   REFERENCES

Friedl, A. (1991). *Teaching science to children.* New York: McGraw-Hill, Inc.

Hapkiewicz, A. & Hapkiewicz, W. (1993). *Misconceptions in science.* Presented at National Science Teachers Association regional meeting, Denver.

Musical instrument recipe book. (1971). Elementary Science Study (ESS). New York: McGraw-Hill.

Oxenhorn, J. (1982). *Pathways to science: sound and light.* New York: Globe Book Company.

Whistles and strings. (1971). Elementary Science Study (ESS). New York: McGraw-Hill.

LIGHT AND COLOR

A.   IDENTIFICATION OF THE CONCEPTS

light, color, wavelength, seeing, reflection, refraction, diffraction, scattering

B.   BACKGROUND INFORMATION FOR THE TEACHER

What is light?

Light is radiant energy which can travel freely through space. There are many kinds of radiant energy (also called electromagnetic waves), including x-rays, ultraviolet and infra-red radiation, radio waves, microwaves, and cosmic radiation. We can see only a small portion of all the different kinds of radiant energy. Since we sometimes refer to other kinds of electromagnetic waves as "light" (e.g., ultraviolet light), we call the small portion of the radiation spectrum that human eyes can see *visible light*. You should keep this distinction in mind, although in this chapter, we simply refer to visible light as "light."

How do we see?

Light is necessary for us to see. Light travels from the *source* (which could be the sun, a campfire, a room light, or light reflected from something else) to an *object*, where some of the light is *reflected* to our eyes. Our eyes do not do any more to <u>receive</u> light than simply wait for it. Only <u>after</u> light enters the eye are the complex biological processes associated with vision set into motion.

Light that is reflected from an object passes through the curved, transparent cornea, a thin fluid-filled anterior (front) chamber, the pupil (which constricts and expands to regulate the amount of light that is admitted), the lens (which focuses the light on the retina), and then the vitreous humor (a gelatinous fluid that fills most of the eyeball) before it reaches the retina. (See Figure I.)

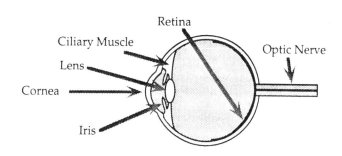

Figure 1

The retina is the delicate film of tissue lining the back of the eye that contains light- and color-sensing neurons. When light hits the retina, it stimulates (excites) these sensory cells (receptors), triggering waves of nerve impulses that are carried along the nerve cells that make up the optic nerve to the brain. The part of the brain that is involved with sight is called the visual cortex, and it is in the brain that the pattern of incoming stimuli is interpreted as vision. In humans, the process of "seeing" results in our awareness of shades of light and dark, perception of color, and images.

What is color?

Because human eyes have both light and color receptors (most mammals have only light receptors), everything we see can be described as having a color; this is also true of light. In fact, it is because visible light has color that we see objects as having different colors. An object that appears red, such as an apple, reflects only red light to our eyes and absorbs all of the other colors—which are all contained in white light. White light, such as sunlight, can be broken down into these colors. The reason for this is that light travels in waves, and our visual system perceives *different wavelengths as different colors*. Each color has a different wavelength, which means that as two waves of different lengths travel the same distance, different numbers of waves will be needed. (See Figure II.)

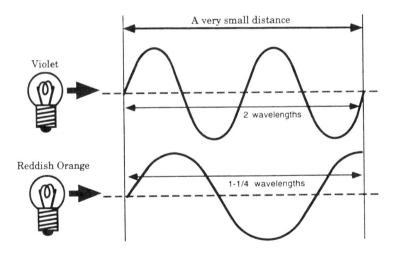

Figure II

When white light is passed through a prism or a soap bubble, different wavelengths are separated from one another, producing the range of colors that we see. Of the light that is visible to us, violet has the shortest wavelength. It takes 25,000 wave oscillations to cross a centimeter. Red has the longest wavelength, but it still takes more than 14,000 oscillations to cross a centimeter. All other colors that we see fall between these two extremes. A prism, which separates light by bending it, bends violet the most and red the least. All other colors are bent more than red but less than violet, producing the smooth spectrum that we see in rainbows.

Not only can white light be separated into many colors, colors can be added together to make white light. Red, green, and blue alone are enough to reconstruct white light, so we call them primary colors. Each primary color can be produced by subtracting the other two primary colors from white light. We see an object's color because the pigments of the object absorb particular wavelengths and reflect only the wavelength of the color our eyes see. This selective reflection effectively subtracts some colors from white light, leaving only the colors that we see.

What are the properties of light?

1. How light travels

Light, as we have said, travels through space as oscillating waves; but we have also noted that these waves are very tiny compared with the objects that we see. Consequently, for all practical purposes, most light phenomena can be explained by ignoring these waves and using the rule "light travels in straight lines." This property of light to travel in a straight path is the reason that we cannot see around a corner. This is also the reason a pinhole camera produces an inverted image. (See Figure III.)

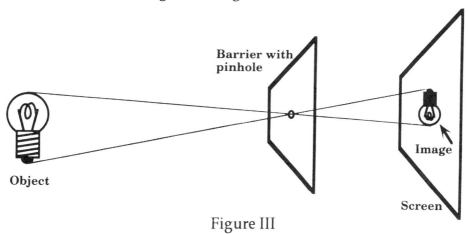

Figure III

2. Reflection

When light strikes a surface, some or all of it is reflected. The angle at which light bounces off (known as the *angle of reflection*) is the same as the angle at which it strikes the surface (known as the *angle of incidence*). Light which strikes a smooth surface at a right angle bounces straight back. (See Figure IV.)

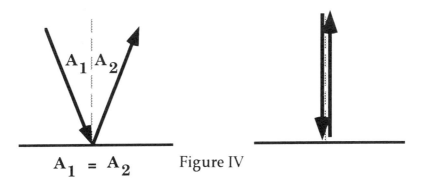

$A_1 = A_2$ Figure IV

Light that strikes a smooth, polished surface such as a mirror is not mixed up by surface roughness and can result in a clearly reflected image. (See Figure V.)

Figure V

3.   Refraction

When a light beam passes from one medium to another, it bends. For example, a light beam which travels from air into a water-filled aquarium is bent, as shown in Figure VI a. This is because the speed of light is different in different media. A line drawn perpendicular to the boundary between two media is called a *normal line*. If a beam speeds up as it travels from one medium to another, it is bent away from the normal line, as in VI b. If a beam slows down, as it does in Figure VI a, it is bent toward the normal line.

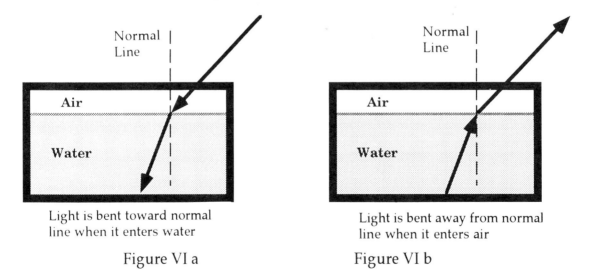

Light is bent toward normal
line when it enters water

Figure VI a

Light is bent away from normal
line when it enters air

Figure VI b

4.   Diffraction

We did not need to think about wavelengths to explain reflection or refraction, but we do need to consider them to explain diffraction. If light passes near the edges of a small opening, it spreads out. Sound, which also is made up of waves, also spreads out. However, with sound a small opening is not needed—noises can be heard around the corner. A light beam, however, cannot travel around a corner without the help of a reflector. The reason for the difference is this: in order to diffract and spread out, the size of the opening must be close to the same size as the wavelength. Light, we have noted, has a very tiny wavelength, so we do not normally notice much diffraction. Sound has a much bigger wavelength than light—about 2 meters. There are many objects in our world that are roughly that size, so we are very familiar with the spreading, or diffraction, of sound.

5.   Scattering

When light hits small particles, such as dust or smoke in the air, it scatters in all directions. As with diffraction, the amount of light scattering depends on the size of the particles and the wavelength of light striking the particles. If the particle size is roughly the same as the wavelength of the light that strikes it, scattering can separate colors. Since colors have different wavelengths, different colors are scattered differently. The sky is blue because the scattering particles are so small that they can efficiently scatter light only toward the violet end of the light spectrum. Red sunsets on earth are the result of light traveling through more atmosphere (laterally) before we see it, as opposed to when we are looking through the atmosphere at a perpendicular angle—up into the sky. So much blue (actually violet) light is scattered by particles in the thick atmosphere at sunset that the sun's white light has the blue completely subtracted out. As a result, it appears red. If there were no atmosphere to scatter the light, the sky would always appear black, day and night. This is how the sky looks on the moon.

If the particle size is bigger than the wavelengths of visible light, waves can be absorbed and *re-emitted* essentially unchanged. Clouds are white because cloud particles are of this size; they scatter all wavelengths of light. If the particle size is too big, then the particles absorb and reflect like other everyday objects and no scattering occurs.

What is a LASER?

H. G. Wells published a book called The War of the Worlds before the turn of the century, which tells a story about Martians invading and nearly conquering the Earth. Their weapon? A mysterious "sword of heat" shooting a "ghost of a beam of light." The beam of light, focused by a curved mirror, dropped men and melted metal.

Decades later, the "sword of heat" comes close to reality in the form of a laser. The word laser is an acronym for Light Amplification by Stimulated Emission of Radiation. A laser "gun" shoots out a narrow, highly concentrated beam of light. Lasers produce the most intense, sharp, pure light ever known. They can be made from the excitation of many different gases, including helium, neon, carbon dioxide, and even the vapor of scotch whiskey.

C. SOME REPRESENTATIVE STUDENT MISCONCEPTIONS ABOUT LIGHT AND COLOR

♦ A light source and its effects are not separate.

♦ White light is colorless and pure.

♦ A color filter adds color to a white beam.

♦ While light is <u>reflected</u> by mirrors, it <u>remains</u> on other objects.

♦ The eye is the active agent in <u>gathering</u> light, rather than being just a receiver of reflected light.

♦ Light helps us see simply by illuminating objects and making them visible.

♦ Shadows are independent of the object causing them.

♦ Magnifying glasses make the light "bigger;" i.e. there is more light on the side of the lens opposite to the source.

D. SOURCES OF STUDENTS' CONFUSION AND MISCONCEPTIONS

♦ Sometimes we are able to see things without an obvious source of light present, such as when we are in a room.

♦ The English language almost always speaks of reflection in terms of mirrors and other smooth, shiny surfaces. Other objects, such as a piece of paper, are rarely spoken of as reflective, even though all objects are.

♦ When we turn on the light in a room, the room "lights up," along with all the objects in it. Light rays are not directly visible, so it is not obvious that light is reflected from things.

♦ When we mix several different colors of paint, we often get a dark, brownish mess. Each color of paint subtracts all other colors but its own. This effect is different than mixing several colors of light, which produces a <u>lighter</u> combination as each color is added to the others.

E. LEARNING ABOUT LIGHT AND COLOR USING THE CONCEPTUAL CHANGE MODEL

TEACHING NOTES

Provide each small group with the following materials:

shoe box
flashlight
2 flat mirrors
1 concave mirror
1 convex mirror
shiny metal spoon
clear beaker or glass
water, oil, saltwater solution
few drops of milk

For Activity III. Color: Theater gels are necessary to get the desired results when mixing light. Gels can usually be purchased at art supply stores. To mix the light colors, place each gel over the end of a separate filmstrip projector or overhead projector. Focus all three lights on the same spot on a white wall or a screen. (This may need to be a whole group activity due to the need for equipment.)

ACTIVITY I: Path of Light

1. Commit to an Outcome

We have the following situation: a shoe box, with a hole cut out at one end and a white sheet of paper (for a screen) taped to the other end. A light source is placed in front of the hole, so that light will travel through the hole and produce an image on the screen. (See Figure 1.)

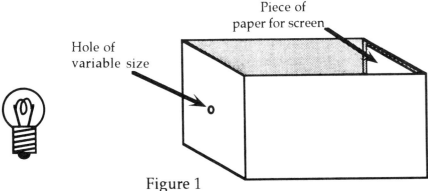

Piece of
paper for screen

Hole of
variable size

Figure 1

What kind of image will we have if the opening is a circle with a diameter of 1 cm? If the opening is a pinhole? Write your comments or make drawings to illustrate your point.

2. Expose Beliefs

Share your predictions, explanations, and drawings with others in your small group. Decide on a spokesperson from your small group to explain your group's predictions with the large group.

3. Confront Beliefs

Test your ideas and those of others by working with the materials.

4. Accommodate the Concept

With your small group, try to resolve any conflicts between your beliefs and your observations. Try to come up with a statement describing the phenomenon presented here.

5. Extend the Concept

Try to think of situations and examples where you have seen light traveling in a straight line in the real world. Can you think of any practical uses for the effect seen in the shoe box experiment?

6. Go Beyond

Try to answer, with the help of the group, any questions you have related to the path of light.

ACTIVITY II: Reflection

1. Commit to an Outcome

A beam of light can be produced by a point source (such as the pinhole in the activity above) or a laser. What will happen if you shine a beam of light on:

   a.   a plane mirror (flat)?
   b.   a concave mirror (curved inward)?
   c.   a convex mirror (curved outward)?

Make predictions by making drawings and giving explanations.

2. Expose Beliefs

Share your drawings and explanations about what will happen to the beams of light with the members of your group.

3. Confront Beliefs

Get the flat, convex, and concave mirrors and use beams of light to test your ideas and explanations.

4. Accommodate the Concept

What did you observe as you tested your ideas? What would happen if you changed the angle and position of the beam with respect to the mirrors? What would happen if several parallel beams shined on each different mirror? What statement can you make about the behavior of light as it hits the surfaces of different shapes?

5. Extend the Concept

Look for reflection in the world around you. In real life, where are these kinds of reflectors used, and why? Where and how do we use reflection in general?

Have you ever looked into a shiny metal spoon? How do you see yourself, and how is it connected to what you have seen here?

How would an object look in two plane mirrors perpendicular to one another? Discuss and then test your ideas.

6. Go Beyond

For the next class, bring examples, questions, or problems based on what you have seen.

ACTIVITY III: Color

1. Commit to an Outcome

What color will result if we mixed green, blue, and red light by projecting them together on the wall? If we blocked one of the three colors, what will result in each case? Think of an explanation to accompany your answer.

2. Expose Beliefs

Share your predictions and ideas about this question with members of your own group. Are there any changes in your answer or explanation that you would like to make after talking with the rest of your group?

3. Confront Beliefs

In your small groups, actually test your ideas by projecting the three colors of light on the wall and examining the results.

4. Accommodate the Concept

With your small group, try to come up with a synthesized reason for what you saw in the experiment. Describe the process of addition and subtraction of colors. If your initial explanations turned out to be wrong, what impression may have led you astray?

5. Extend the Concept

What are some of the phenomena related to color with which you are familiar? How would you apply what has been discussed here to how we perceive color? How would you explain the fact that if you stare at a bright color for 30 seconds and then look at a white sheet, you see a different color?

As with reflection, see if you can find examples of color variation in the world around you. (For example, does an object always appear to have the same color?)

6. Go Beyond

Bring additional examples and questions on color to the next class period.

ACTIVITY IV: Refraction

A. <u>The effect of a liquid on the path of a beam</u>

1. Commit to an Outcome

What will happen if you shine a beam of light into an empty container, and, as you are looking at the beam, add water to the container? What if, instead of water, you add another liquid, such as oil? Salt water? Write your ideas or make drawings to show what you think would happen to the appearance of the beam.

2. Expose Beliefs

In your small group, share your beliefs as to what will happen to the beam of light as you add water or the other liquids to the container.

3. Confront Beliefs

Test your ideas about the effect of the added liquid on the beam by trying it with containers, liquids, and light beams. How well did you do?

B. <u>The effect of a liquid on the appearance of a penny in a container</u>

1. Commit to an Outcome

What will happen if you place a penny under an empty container, and–as you are looking at the penny–add water to the container? What if, instead of water, you add oil? Salt water? Write your predictions or make drawings to illustrate your ideas.

2. Expose Beliefs

In your small group, share your beliefs about what will happen to the appearance of the penny as you add water and the other liquids to the empty container. Appoint a group member to report your small group's thoughts to the class

3. Confront Beliefs

Test your ideas and those of your group members by working with containers, pennies and different liquids.

C. The effect of eyeglasses on a beam of light

1. Commit to an Outcome

Get into a group of 3 or 4 where at least one member of the group wears glasses. As a group, examine the glasses. Without asking the wearer whether he or she is near-sighted or far-sighted, try to guess the answer and give reasons for your decision. Feel free to use beams of light or other means to help you arrive at a conclusion.

2. Expose Beliefs

Share your predictions and reasons with members of your group, and before the friend who wears the glasses gives the answer, have a representative present the various predictions and explanations to the large group.

3. Confront Beliefs

Now simply ask your friend if he or she is near-sighted or far-sighted. In your group and with the help of the friend wearing glasses, try to explain your observations.

4. Accommodate the Concept

How can the shape of the glasses helps one's vision? Are there any common effects that appear in the three activities (beam of light, penny, and eyeglasses)? What statement can we make about the phenomenon involved here?

5. Extend the Concept

Where have you seen examples of light bending as it goes from one medium to another? Where do we make use of the refraction phenomena?

6. Go Beyond

Between now and the next session, see if you can come up with other examples or additional questions and problems on refraction that you would like to investigate and bring them to class to share.

ACTIVITY V: Scattering

1. Commit to an Outcome

If we add a few drops of milk to a beaker filled with water, what color will appear if we shine light perpendicular to the beaker? Individually make a prediction and give reasons for your predictions.

2. Expose Beliefs

Share your predictions and explanations about the color produced by shining light on the beaker. Then have a representative from your group present your group's answers to the class.

3. Confront Beliefs

Test your ideas and those of others by testing them with the beaker of water, milk, and a flashlight.

4. Accommodate the Concept

By sharing your ideas and raising questions, resolve conflict between what you believed would happen and what did happen. What statement can you make summarizing the concept in your own words?

5. Extend the Concept

What examples can you provide as to where this phenomenon occurs in nature?

6. Go Beyond

How could the experiment above be extended and modified? What would result from these modifications? Pursue any unanswered questions to determine the answers.

F.   REFERENCES

Eaton, J., Anderson, C., & Smith, E. (1984). Students' misconceptions interfere with science learning: case studies of fifth grade students. *The Elementary School Journal, 84(4)*, 365-379.

Eaton, J. , Anderson, C. , & Smith, E. (1983). When students don't know they don't know. *Science and Children, 20(7)*, 6-9.

Feher, E., & Rice, K. (1986). Shadow shapes. *Science and Children, 24(2)*, 6-9.

Guesne, E. (1984). Children's ideas about light. In *New Trends in Physics Teaching, Vol. IV*. Paris: UNESCO.

Guesne, E. (1984). Light. In *New Trends in Physics Teaching, Vol. IV.* Paris: UNESCO.

Iona, M. & Beaty, W. (1987). Reflections on refraction. *Science and Children, 25*, 18-20.

Liem, T. (1987). *Invitation to science inquiry.* Lexington MA: Ginn Press.

Watts, D. (1985). Student conceptions of light: a case study. *Physics Education, 20*, 183-187.

TRANSFORMATION OF ENERGY

A.   IDENTIFICATION OF THE CONCEPTS

Definition of energy, transformation of energy, types of energy, properties of energy, applications of energy, importance of energy

B.   BACKGROUND INFORMATION FOR THE TEACHER

<u>What is energy?</u>

Unlike matter and many physical phenomena, energy is intangible. We can perceive the *results* of energy transfers and transformations, but we can't actually sense energy itself. Since it is intangible, it is not very simple to define; but, since energy is a very important idea, let us try. If we were to make an attempt to define it, we might say that <u>energy</u> is the ability of matter to bring about changes.

Instead of spending considerable amount of time defining energy, however, let us concentrate on what it does. An example of energy bringing about change is when an egg is cooked. Heat (or thermal) energy from the stove brings about change in the egg—part of it changes from clear to white and from gooey to semi-solid because the heat changes the physical characteristics of the egg-white protein molecules (albumin). Other examples are when a moving ocean wave pushes you over, and when the heat energy of a candle changes ice to water and water to steam.

<u>What is energy transformation?</u>

All physical events involve transforming energy from one form to another, such as radiant to electrical, chemical to mechanical, potential to kinetic, etc. When electrical current passes through a light bulb, electrical energy is transformed into light energy and heat energy. When a boulder begins to roll downhill, potential energy is transformed into kinetic energy. A complex example of energy transformation is when food is changed by the body cells into energy used to grow, think, and play.

Objects and substances can store energy in physical and chemical forms. Food, batteries, a tight spring, and gasoline all store energy. Physical and chemical changes may require energy in order to occur or may release energy. In living organisms, all biological processes involve chemical energy and reactions.

<u>What are different kinds of energy?</u>

A motor is run by electrical energy, and when you talk on the telephone, your voice is sent over thousands of miles of space using this same kind of energy. Chemical energy runs our cars. Batteries provide electrical energy but start with chemical energy. Mechanical energy is released when water goes over a waterfall. A rock precariously placed on the edge of a cliff also has mechanical energy, even though it is not moving. One small push and that energy could be released!

We will take the advice of Taber (1989) and limit the forms of energy we consider in these activities to the following examples:

(a) Kinetic energy	pop-fly baseball, moving water
(b) Sound energy	thunderclap, rock concert, sound of the wind
(c) Thermal energy	boiling water, dark car in the sun, geysers
(d) Radiation energy	light, infrared, radio waves, x-rays
(e) Potential energy	gravity, chemicals, magnets
(f) Electrical current energy	lightning, house outlets, calculators

What are the sources and properties of energy?

The *sun* is a major source of energy for changes on the earth's surface. The sun's energy arrives as radiation in a range of wavelengths, consisting mainly of visible light with significant amounts of infrared and ultraviolet radiation. The heat of solar infrared radiation drives the earth's atmospheric and oceanic currents, influencing climate and weather patterns. Specific bands of visible light wavelengths are the source of virtually all food energy to fuel biological processes on the earth, through the energy conversion reactions of photosynthesis.

Scientists believe that the *universe* contains all the matter and energy that ever existed; thus energy is not being created during physical and chemical phenomena. The structure of the universe is the result of interactions involving fundamental particles and basic forces.

Just as it is not being created, energy is not being destroyed. Energy is *conserved*—when it is used, it does not just disappear. Whenever energy is reduced in one place, it is increased somewhere else by exactly the same amount.

Energy also can be *transformed* (changed) from one form to another, as in the examples above. These ideas are a little hard to understand at first, because energy can be sneaky in how it changes from one form to another. When we run a battery-powered toy car, energy is changed from chemical energy to electrical energy in the batteries, and this electrical energy runs the motor. The motor changes electrical energy to mechanical energy, and the wheels turn. Then where does the energy go? Lots of places. The sound of the car running represents a form of energy. If you bump the car into the wall, it makes more sound energy. The wheels rubbing on the ground release a little bit of heat energy. If the car knocks down a stack of building blocks, more energy has been converted. So, when the batteries are dead, it isn't that the energy is gone. The energy has just become too spread out to be usable. As stated earlier and demonstrated by this example, energy can be converted from one kind to another, and it is conserved—it can be accounted for.

When energy is transformed from one kind to another, some of it may change to *heat*. After rubbing two surfaces together rapidly, you may be able to feel the heat that is generated. When you work out, heat is released as your body converts chemical energy (food) to mechanical energy (muscle contraction); as a result, your body temperature rises and you may begin sweating, facilitating heat transfer by evaporation.

Why is energy important?

Energy is important because it is involved in everything we do. Being alive requires energy. When we want to go somewhere, whether by bicycle, car, train, or plane, we use energy. When we want to read a book at night, we use energy. When we want to keep warm in the wintertime, we use energy. But energy is even more important than that. As we saw in the example with the toy car, using one form of energy sometimes changes it into other forms of energy that are useless to us and that may even have negative effects on us and our environment. For example, excess heat may be unloaded into the atmosphere, rivers, lakes, and oceans. Potentially toxic or otherwise harmful molecules may be synthesized and contribute to air and water pollution or cause damage to plant and animal tissues.

Also, we have developed an energy-intensive world civilization, relying heavily on the burning of fossil fuels (coal, oil, and natural gas) to produce electrical energy that is used in turn to produce mechanical energy to power our machines. The earth has coal, oil and natural gas under its surface, but not an unlimited amount. Once it is used up, those things that are powered by these fossil fuels will have to be powered by another source. While it may be a long time before the fossil fuels are completely used up, understanding energy allows us to design ways to use it more efficiently and make fossil fuels last longer. Ultimately, understanding energy very well might lead us to energy sources that are unlikely to run out for an unbelievably long time. Efficient use of abundant, nonpolluting solar energy is one of these alternatives, and a fully safe method of using nuclear energy may be another alternative.

C. SOME REPRESENTATIVE STUDENT MISCONCEPTIONS ABOUT ENERGY

♦ Many students believe that energy is only associated with human beings or things that have human attributes.

♦ There are two categories of objects—those that have energy and those that need it. For example, a battery has energy and a bulb needs energy to light.

♦ Energy is not stored in food. Food only gives you energy when you eat it.

♦ Energy is not conserved because it is like a waste product similar to smoke or sweat.

♦ A person pushing a box has energy, but the box can't have energy. ("If it did, it would help the person!" is a typical response.)

♦ Stored energy is something that causes energy later. It is not energy until it has been released.

♦ Force and energy are the same thing; for example, a coiled spring has a hidden force and a falling rock has "force."

♦ Energy is a substantive entity.

♦ Students strongly associate force and movement with energy but few associate it with the scientific concept of work.

D. SOURCES OF STUDENTS' CONFUSION AND MISCONCEPTIONS

♦ The word "energy" has many connotations in everyday language.

♦ The introduction of the term "work" brings its everyday connotation to the meaning of energy and confuses the issue. People, ships, and hammers have energy because they do work for us, but rolling rocks and clouds don't do anything for us; therefore, they can't have energy.

♦ The common treatment of energy as a fluid gives the idea that it is something that is conducted, transported, or poured in.

♦ For many students the statement that energy is neither created nor destroyed, (i.e., that it is conserved) may mean something literal and restricted, such as what happens to a piece of clay when its shape is changed

♦ Memorization of principles such as conservation of energy actually causes more difficulty for "academically good students" than for those students who have not shown interest in learning the principles or memorizing them.

♦ A student's notion of energy is influenced by his or her experiences with the physical world and the resulting intuitive ideas.

♦ The large and varied concept of energy (energy transformation, energy conservation, and energy degradation) is abstract and conceptually difficult for many students.

♦ Use of the phrases "energy is used," "using energy," or "energy is lost" do not imply conservation of energy. In reality, the energy is transferred.

♦ Approaching energy through the notion of work may result in students grounding their ideas about energy in terms of observable characteristics such as force and distance rather than on energy conservation.

♦ The idealized treatment of energy in books, particularly when speaking of conservation of energy and ignoring friction and other forms such as heat, may cause difficulty.

♦ In describing energy, we often use more than one word for the same idea.

♦ In describing energy, we often use the same word to describe several different things.

◆ Words that have particular meanings are used casually in ways that are not strictly valid.

◆ Inconsistency among different presentations by teachers and books causes confusion. Taber has identified over 80 different terms for energy found in books. Examples:

atomic	binding	bonding
chemical	chemical action	chemical potential
coal	current	dissociation
dynamic	earth's thermal	EHF
elastic potential	electric	electric potential
electrical	electical potential	electric current
electronic	electostatic	electromagnetic waves
electronic	Fermi	fission
food	free surface	fueling
gamma radiation	gamma-rays	geothermal
gravitational potential	heat	HF
hydrodynamic	hydroelectric	hydroelectricity
infra-red	infra-red (heat) waves	infra-red rays
infra-red waves	infra-red radiation	infra-red waves
internal	internal kinetic	internal potential
internal (vibrational)	ionization	kinetic
latent chemical	LF	light waves
magnetic	magnetism	mass
mechanical	MF	microwaves
muscular	natural gas	Newtonian kinetic
nonmechanical	nuclear	nuclear electricity
photon	potential	proper
relativistic kinetic	respiratory	rest
rotational	rotational kinetic	SHF
solar	solar radiation	sound
sound waves	spring	stored
stored gravitational	strain	thermodynamic
thermonuclear	threshold	tidal
total	total internal	total mechanical
translational	translational kinetic	UHF
ultra-violet	ultra-violet light	ultra-violet radiation
ultra-violet rays	ultra-violet waves	uphill
VHF	vibrational	vibrational kinetic
visible light	VLF	volcanic
waves	wind	work
X-radiation	X-rays	zero point

E.   CONCEPT MAPPING—ANOTHER TEACHING STRATEGY

About Concept Mapping

In addition to the 6-step teaching for conceptual change model (CCM), some of the activities in the Energy section will make use of a teaching strategy called **concept mapping.** The strategy was first established by Novak and Gowin and described in detail in their book titled *Learning How To Learn.* According to these authors, concept mapping is a schematic device for representing a set of concept meanings embedded in a framework of propositions. The maps make it clear to both students and teachers the key ideas they must focus on for any specific learning. Novak and Gowin think of a concept map as a visual road map, showing some of the pathways one may take to connect meanings of concepts in propositions. It may also be a schematic summary of what has been learned.

In this section, concept maps will be used to do the following:

◆   Help students become aware of their own knowledge about a concept, its components, and its relationships to other concepts.

◆   Provide students the opportunity to share ideas with others.

◆   Encourage students to make revisions in their personal understanding of the concept using ideas from others and available resources.

◆   Make sense of the concept and its relationship with other concepts.

◆   Extend the concept by bringing examples and applications.

◆   Go beyond the discussion by asking additional questions and posing other problems to pursue.

Introducing concept mapping to students

Before using concept mapping in the energy activities, you may go through an exercise with your students on a more familiar concept, such as plants. Even though this concept can get very sophisticated, keep it at the students' level, working with their own terms and connections. Remember, this first attempt emphasizes how to do concept mapping rather than the science content.

The following explains how an introductory concept mapping lesson could be done using the topic of plants:

The students were asked to think of as many terms as they could about plants. Some of the terms the children proposed included: green, flower, poisonous, stem, water, light, roots, photosynthesis, edible, seeds, dirt, food, fertilizer, leaves, and sun.

The teacher introduced words such as: is, are, made of, have, need, when, and produce. Students were told these could be used as linking words to connect some of the terms they had listed. Students were given the opportunity to propose other linking words.

Using the terms and the linking words, the students constructed short sentences similar to the following:

Most plants are green.   Plants need sun.
Plants need fertilizer.   Plants grow through photosynthesis.
Plants grow from seeds.   Some plants are edible.
Plants have stems.   Plants need water.
Plants have roots.   Plants need air.
Plants have leaves.   Some plants are poisonous.

Using students sentences, the following concept map was constructed by the teacher with input from the students.

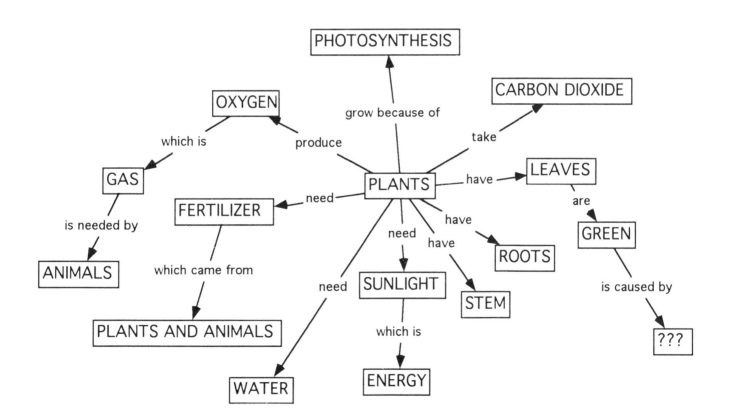

The students were encouraged to connect other concepts. Then the students constructed their own concept maps on other topics, shared their maps with others, and revised them using ideas from others, activities, or reading materials.

In the energy section, activities II, IV, and VIII and outside projects #2 and #4 make use of concept mapping.

F.   LEARNING ABOUT ENERGY USING THE CONCEPTUAL CHANGE MODEL, CONCEPT MAPPING, AND PROJECTS

TEACHING NOTES

As students go through each activity, encourage them to concentrate on the following observations about energy:

> What is the source causing what we observe; i.e., what makes it happen?
> How does it manifest itself?
> What was accomplished?
> Why does it run out?
> Was it all useful? If not, how was it wasted?
> Was there evidence of transformation? If so, what was it?

Provide each group with the following materials as needed:

> variety of spheres
> materials to construct inclines
> sliders (small paper cups cut in half vertically)
> candles
> safety matches
> pieces of various colors of felt or fabric
> thermometers
> small board
> rods of copper, aluminum, and brass (various diameters, lengths of each)
> wires
> Pyrex
> string
> pendulum bobs (2 identical)
> gravel, rock, salt, shredded newspaper, water, sawdust, sand, soil
> styrofoam cups
> 1.5 volt battery
> flashlight bulbs
> short copper wires
> copper wire approximately 30 cm long

G.   OUTSIDE ACTIVITIES FOR STUDENTS

Another feature of this section is outside projects for students. Some possible ideas are:

1.   Have students determine operating costs of electric appliances

2.   Ask students to make a concept map of energy transfers and transformations in such items as:

> a mechanical or electric toy
> toaster
> refrigerator
> solar calculator
> blender
> clock
> color TV
> microwave oven

3.   Ask students to keep track of some aspect of energy (pathways, uses, transformations, amounts, etc.) at home or at school for an entire day.

4.   Have students make concept maps of an energy system they have created themselves.

ACTIVITY I.   Rolling Spheres

1.   Commit to an Outcome

Having access to all kinds of spheres and inclines, what situation do you predict would cause the slider to move the farthest? Why do you think so?

2.   Expose Beliefs

Share your prediction with others in your group and give your reasons. Working with others in your group, decide on a plan as to how you can investigate your ideas.

3.   Confront Beliefs

Set up appropriate experimental situations to collect necessary data.

4.   Accommodate the Concept

Based on the data that you have collected, what statement can you make about the concept involved? As you listen to the presentations of others, what changes do you want to make in your own statement?

What have you concluded about the following questions:
What causes the sphere to begin to move?
What is the role of the mass of the sphere?
What is the role of the angle?
What is the role of the position of release?
What causes the sphere to stop?

5.   Extend the Concept

What are some other examples (applications) of what you have observed here?

6.   Go Beyond

What are some of the questions (problems) related to the concept you want to pursue? How would you set up your investigation to pursue the problems (questions) you have identified?

Ball
Ruler
Paper Cup
Cut in Half

Ruler
Ball
Paper Cup Moved

ACTIVITY II. Lighting a Candle
Concept Mapping

1. Become Aware of One's Ideas

With a candle and match in sight, think about everything that is involved when we strike the match and light the candle. Write down as many terms as you can that describe what is involved. Then write down some words that can be used to connect the terms you have thought about. Using the terms and the connectors, write down some sentences. Use your sentences to construct a concept map illustrating your ideas about what is involved in the candle and match system.

2. Share Ideas with Others

Share your maps with others in your group. Work with group members to construct a group map. Have someone present the group map to the rest of the class.

3. Accommodate Ideas and Discussion

As others present their maps, make appropriate additions to your map, and use appropriate resources to add to the map. Use different colored markers to make the revisions in your map so you can see both the original ideas and the modified ideas.

4. Make Sense of the Concept in Your Own Words

Using ideas from others and appropriate resources, describe the system in terms of the following questions:

What is the source of the fire created by the match?
How are the fire and light transferred to the candle?
What makes the candle burn?
What happens to the light and heat when the candle is used up?

5. Extend the Concept

What are some examples of similar systems which you are familiar?

6. Go Beyond

What are some additional questions and problems that you could pursue related to this phenomenon?

ACTIVITY III. What Color is Best?

For this activity you are provided a board, pieces of some materials (felt or cloth) of different colors, and thermometers.

1. Commit to an Outcome

Predict which color will get warm the fastest when exposed to the energy source. What color will collect the most heat? What color will retain heat the longest? Provide reasons for your predictions.

2. Expose Beliefs

Share your predictions and explanations with others in your group. Have someone from your group present to the large group the predictions and explanations of the individuals.

3. Confront Beliefs

Get the necessary materials and work with your group to test your ideas and those of others. Based on your observations, what changes can you make in your ideas about which color or colors collect and keep the heat the longest?

4. Accommodate the Concept

Using the results of the experimental tests and the discussions, what statements can you make about the role of color in collecting and retaining heat?

5. Extend the Concept

What are some applications of what you have observed here? How are your observations related to the color of clothes people wear in different parts of the world?

6. Go Beyond

What are some additional questions and problems you can investigate related to this concept?

ACTIVITY IV.a   Inside a Battery
Concept Mapping

You have a container of diluted acid. A strip of zinc and a strip of copper are placed in the acid with a light bulb connected to them. Once connected, the light bulb will light.

1. Become Aware of Your Own Ideas

Write down some of the terms associated with this system. What are some linking words that can be used to connect the terms? Make sentences using the terms and linking words you have identified.

Using your sentences, make a concept map to show what you think happens inside this system.

2. Share Ideas

Share your map with others in your group. Work with group members to construct a group map. Have one member of the group present the group map to the rest of the class.

3. Accommodate the Ideas and Discussion

Using ideas from others, making observations, and consulting appropriate resources, a make appropriate changes in the map (using a different colored marker).

4. Make Sense of the Concept in Your Own Way

What statements can be made about the science concept involved in this system?

5. Extend the Concept

What are some examples of and applications of the phenomenon?

6. Go Beyond

Write down some questions or problems that you can pursue related to this concepts.

ACTIVITY IV. b   An Electric Cell

NOTE: This activity is written to the teacher rather than to the student. It is more appropriate for junior high and high school students than for elementary students. The situations described should be set up as demonstrations by the teacher, who then leads students through the discussion using the questions posed on the following page.

Each situation to be described to students (and set up as demonstration) consists of a beaker, electrodes, connecting wires, and a bulb or an ammeter. The drawings below illustrate the specific materials for each situation.

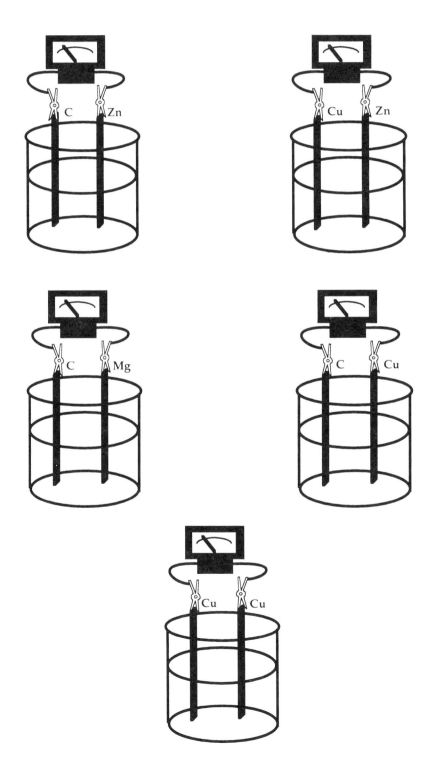

1. Commit to an Outcome

Have students predict which situation would give the highest reading of the ammeter (or brightest bulb) and which will be the weakest reading of the ammeter (or dimmest bulb) if a certain amount of acid is poured into each beaker and wires are connected, Encourage students to provide explanations (reasons) for their predictions.

2. Expose Beliefs

Have them share their predictions and explanations with the rest of the class.

3. Confront Beliefs

Test their predictions by pouring the diluted acid (possibly H_2SO_4) and connecting the wires and the meter or bulb

4. Accommodate the Concepts

Ask questions and encourage discussion to help remove the conflict between their predictions or explanations and their observations.

Develop the concept that electrodes, prior to adding the acid, are neutral.

Develop the concepts of reactions, products (H_2 and energy), electronegativity of different electrodes, etc.

Develop the concepts of:
    electric pressure (voltage)
    current (in terms of motion of charges)
    resistance

5. Extend the Concept

Encourage students to extend the idea to other situations with which they may be familiar.

6. Go Beyond

Encourage students to think of some additional questions (problems) they would like to pursue related to the concept.

ACTIVITY V.   What Material and Type of Rod Best Conduct Heat?

You will be given rods of the same length, made of copper, aluminum, and brass. There will be a variety of thin, thick, solid, and hollow rods. You will also be given wires and Pyrex.

1.   Commit to an Outcome

Which object/material would conduct heat the fastest? Make predictions and give reasons for your predictions.

2.   Expose Beliefs

Share your predictions and explanations with others in your group.

3.   Confront Beliefs

Get the necessary materials. Decide how you would test your predictions and those of others. Test your ideas and revise your explanations, if necessary.

4.   Accommodate the Concept

Using the results of observations and discussions, what statement can be made about the type of material and rod which conducts heat fastest?

5.   Extend the Concept

What are some applications of this phenomenon?

6.   Go Beyond

What other questions or problems can be pursued related to this phenomenon?

ACTIVITY VI. The Twin Pendulum

Two equal, identical pendulums are set up as shown here.

1. Commit to an Outcome

What will happen to the second pendulum if you pull on one of the pendulums and release it? Make your predictions and give reasons for your predictions.

2. Expose Beliefs

Share your predictions and explanations with others in your group.

3. Confront Beliefs

Get the necessary materials, set up the twin pendulums, and test your ideas. What did you observe happening to the second pendulum? Analyze your observation of the system in terms of energy transformation, production, conservation, and other ideas.

4. Accommodate the Concept

Using the results of your observations and discussion, what statements can you make about the energy involved in a twin pendulum system?

5. Extend the Concept

What are some familiar examples and applications of this phenomenon.?

6. Go Beyond

Write down some problems and questions you may want to pursue. For instance, you may consider variations in the mass of the bob of one or both of the pendulums, the length of the string of one or both pendulums, and the material that makes up the crosspiece to which both pendulums are connected.

ACTIVITY VII. What Material is the Best Solar Collector?

You will work with gravel, rock salt, shredded newspaper, water, sawdust, sand, dirt, Styrofoam cups, and thermometers.

1. **Commit to an Outcome**

Which material will reach the highest temperature? Which will retain the heat the longest? Which will lose heat the quickest?

2. **Expose Beliefs**

Share your predictions and explanations with others in your group. Listen to the ideas of other group members.

3. **Confront Beliefs**

Get the necessary materials to test your ideas and the ideas of other group members. Based on your observations, what changes do you want to make in your initial explanations?

4. **Accommodate the Concepts**

What statements can you make about the properties of the materials and their ability to collect and retain solar energy?

5. **Extend the Concept**

What applications and examples of this concept are you familiar with? What materials would work the best as a heat storage wall in a passive solar home? Think about your ideas related to these questions.

6. **Go Beyond**

What other questions, problems, or projects would you like to pursue related to this?

ACTIVITY VIII. Light and Plant Growth
Concept Mapping

1.   Become Aware of Your Own Ideas

Make a concept map of the role of light in plant growth.

2.   Share Ideas

Share your map with others in the group. Then construct a group map. Have one person from your group presents the group's map to the rest of the class.

3.   Accommodate Ideas and Discussions

Using ideas from other groups, resources, and materials, make revisions in the concept map. Use a different colored marker for your revisions so you can compare the revised version to your original ideas.

4.   Make Sense of the Concept In Your Own Way

What statements can you make about the concepts in this phenomenon?

5.   Extend the Concept

Identify examples and extensions of the concept.

6.   Go Beyond

Identify questions and problems to pursue related to the concept.

ACTIVITY IX. Lighting a Bulb

A complete circuit consists of a battery, a piece of wire, and a light bulb (which lights when the circuit is properly connected). Figure A shows such a circuit.

A   B

1. **Commit to an Outcome**

Predict what would happen if you connected the poles of the battery with a short wire on the other side (Figure B). Give reasons for your predictions

2. **Expose Beliefs**

Share your predictions and reasons with others in your small group.

3. **Confront Beliefs**

Gather the necessary materials to test your predictions. Make changes in your explanations, if necessary.

4. **Accommodate the Concept**

Based on discussions and observations, respond to the following:
>   What is the source of light and heat?
>   What is the transformation involved?
>   What makes it continue?
>   What makes it run out?
>   What is the role of the wire in the circuit?
>   What is the explanation?
>   Is there a difference in transformation?

5. **Extend the Concept**

What are some examples (applications) of the concept?

6. **Go Beyond**

What are some questions or problems related to this concept that you can pursue?

ACTIVITY X. Putting Out a Flame

1. Commit to an Outcome

You have access to matches, a candle, and a single piece of copper wire. Your challenge is, without blowing on the candle flame, pouring water, or touching the wick, to put out the flame by using a single piece of copper wire. (You can do anything to the wire you wish). Give reasons for what you have decided.

2. Expose Beliefs

Share your plan with others in your group. Based on reactions of others, do you want to make any changes in the plan? Have someone from your group present the ideas and plans of the individual members to the rest of the class.

3. Confront Beliefs

Get the necessary materials OR have the teacher demonstrate the plans proposed by different people. As you make your observations, think about the changes you want to make in your design and rationale.

4. Accommodate the Concept

Based on what you observed and on group and class discussions, what statements can you make about the shape of the wire and its effect on the flame?

5. Extend the Concept

What are some examples and applications of this concept?

6. Go Beyond

What are some questions or problems that you can pursue related to this concept? One question may be: Does the type of material the wire is made of (aluminum, copper, iron) have an effect on the results?

ACTIVITY XI. Transformation of energy

1. Commit to an outcome

Of solar, wind, geothermal, and water energy, which resource is best in its potential to be transformed to usable energy for household use? Why do you think so?

2. Expose beliefs

Share your views with the others in your small group. Then, have a representative from your group share the ideas of everyone in your group with the larger group.

3. Confront views

Each member of your group could be assigned to one of the alternative energy sources (solar power, wind power, geothermal, hydropower) to research and bring information on the following aspects:

> What is the source of the energy?
> What transformation is there from energy source to electrical power?
> What are the advantages and limitations of each energy source?

4. Accommodate the concept

Based on what the entire class has learned collectively, what statements can be made about the energy alternative that has best potential for transformation into usable household energy?

5. Extend the concept

Give some examples and applications of alternative energy sources that are of interest to you.

6. Go beyond

What are some questions or problems that you would like to pursue about alternative energy sources? What steps will you take to pursue these questions or problems?

ACTIVITY XII. Energy and recycling

1. Commit to an outcome

You have a choice of paper, glass, aluminum, or plastic for packaging various goods. Which material do you think is best for recycling? Write down your ideas and provide reasons for your choice.

2. Expose beliefs

Share your views and explanations with others in your group. Ask someone in the group to present everyone's ideas to the whole class.

3. Confront beliefs

Obtain as much information as you can about the energy that is needed to recycle each kind of material.

4. Accommodate the concept

Based on what you have learned from your information sources, negotiate with others in your group about whether paper, glass, aluminum, or plastic is a better candidate for recycling.

5. Extend the concept

What are some implications of your discussions and what you have learned about energy and recycling?

6. Go beyond

What are some additional questions or problems that you would like to pursue about the relationship between recycling and energy? What steps will you take to begin pursuing your questions or problems?

REFERENCES

Benchmarks for Science Literacy (1993). New York: Oxford University Press.

Driver, R. & Warrington, L. (1985). Students' use of the principle of energy conservation in problem situations. *Physics Education*, 20 .

Elementary Science Study (ESS). *(1968).Heating and cooling.* New York: McGraw-Hill.

Exploring Energy, 18 (4)(Winter, 1994). Published by the Exploratorium, San Francisco, CA.

Kruger, C., Palacio, D. & Summers, M. (1992). Surveys of English primary teachers' conceptions of force, energy and materials. *Science Education,* 76(4), 339-351.

Novak, J. & Gowin, D. (1984). *Learning How to Learn.* Cambridge University Press.

Science For All Students: The Florida preK-12 Science Curriculum Framework, November 1993.

Solomon, Joan (1985). Teaching the conservation of energy. *The Institute of Physics,* 20.

Taber, Keith (1989). Energy—by many other names. *School Science Review,* 70 (252), 57-62.

The National Science Education Standards (Nov., 1994 Draft). National Academy Press.

Watts, Michael (1983). Some alternative views of energy. *Physics Education,* 18, 213-216.

MORE RECENT CONCEPTS

A. IDENTIFICATION OF THE CONCEPTS

The National Science Education Standards (NSES) identify the following physical science concepts as being important for students in grades 9-12: structure of the atom; elements; chemical reactions; nuclear fission and fusion; kinetic molecular theory; chemical bonds; mass-energy relationships; theory of relativity; electromagnetic waves; entropy and disorder; and quantum theory.

B. BACKGROUND INFORMATION FOR THE TEACHER

The latest national standards for physical science indicate that topics such as those identified above should be addressed in grades 9-12. This chapter provides only an *introduction* to each concept presented. By no means is it suggested that what is presented here is sufficient for secondary students. The teacher is encouraged to use this introduction here as a basis to build upon, using additional strategies and resources.

Adapting the conceptual change strategy

Most of the concepts addressed so far in this book lend themselves to using the 6-step conceptual change strategy. Because the concepts in this chapter are abstract in nature, however, and cannot be easily observed, we will adapt the way the conceptual change strategy is implemented, as shown below.

1. Each student gives an opinion and explains by writing a statement, making a drawing, or building a model.

2. Students share their views with others, first in their small groups and then with the entire class.

3. Students confront their ideas by checking historical perspectives, observing demonstrations, consulting experts or Internet sources, and/or conducting experiments.

4. Students begin to make sense of what they have read or observed and, in their group, negotiate an explanation. They go through the process of resolving conflict between what they thought and what they read by asking "What is the evidence?" and "How do scientists know?", observing additional demonstrations, performing additional experiments.

5. Students provide examples and applications of the concept, or respond to examples and applications provided by the teacher.

6. Students raise additional questions and pose problems to pursue.

Working with abstractions

The authors of the NSES and other scientists and science educators recommend that high school students develop three domains of thought:

Macroscopic world of observable phenomena,
Microscopic world of molecules, atoms, and subatomic particles, and
Symbolic world of chemical formulas, equations, and symbols.

The study of abstract concepts such as atoms and molecules requires that students construct knowledge about particles they cannot see, relying on indirect observations of data and models. While most students will be able to communicate their understanding of physical models, fewer of them will be able to make inferences about atomic structure.

Further, chemistry requires students to communicate their understanding in symbolic form and to solve problems using mathematics. Because many concepts involve knowledge about particles the students will never see, reviewing classical chemistry investigations can be a valuable way for students to build foundations for "how do we know" and "what is the evidence." These investigations provide an historical perspective on developing models, as well as define the chain of evidence that leads us to express confidence in the atomic theory. In addition, teaching with historical vignettes enables us to avoid asking students to believe without seeing.

Structure of the atom

Everything around us is made of very small particles of matter, atoms, that have distinct physical/chemical characteristics. The *Periodic Table of Elements* identifies more than 100 elements. Atoms of elements combine to form molecules; a molecule may be made of atoms of a single element or of several elements.

It is a challenge to visualize the structure of an atom, which is composed of even smaller, active particles. Some models relate the atom to a miniature solar system, in which the Sun represents the nucleus of the atom, surrounded by empty space within which tiny, negatively charged electrons represent the planets that orbit the Sun.

The atomic nucleus consists of positively charged particles called protons, and neutrons, which are neutral (have neither a negative or positive charge) particles that have the same mass as the proton. All of the atoms of a given element have the same number of protons. The mass of a proton is about 1800 times the mass of an electron. Other nuclear particles include mesons, neutrinos, hyperons, and other antiparticles, which are given off in nuclear reactions.

Nuclear fission and fusion

In 1939, Hahn and Strassmann found that the nucleus of a uranium atom can be split into two parts of about the same mass, releasing a great amount of energy in the process. This splitting or fission of the nucleus occurs when uranium is bombarded by neutrons, fired at it like nuclear "bullets." Uranium atoms exist in forms that have different atomic masses, called isotopes. The uranium isotope having a mass of 235, rather than uranium 238, undergoes fission.

A more powerful process, called fusion, occurs by forcing the combination (fusing) of lighter-weight nuclei to form heavier nuclei. Fusion reactions are often called thermonuclear reactions because they take place at temperatures higher than 100 million degrees C. The sun's energy comes from the fusion of hydrogen atoms, forming helium atoms and releasing small particles called positrons.

Elements

An element is the simplest form of matter—it is a substance that contains only one kind of atom. Elements cannot be decomposed into simpler varieties of matter. Prior to the 1500s, only twelve elements were known. Between 1557 and 1925, seventy or so elements were discovered. Since 1937, another eighteen have been discovered.

Every substance we know is made of elements. Most of the elements are solid at ordinary temperatures, while some are liquid and others are gaseous. Some elements are plentiful, while others are more rare; e.g., the distribution of elements in nature is about 50% oxygen, 26% silicon, 7% aluminum, and 17% all the other elements. Some elements, such as copper, gold, and silver, may be found as "free elements," uncombined with other elements. Most of the elements are found in nature, but a few are synthesized in the laboratory. Some of the naturally occurring elements and all of the synthesized elements are radioactive.

Each element has a symbol, consisting of one or two letters. The *Periodic Table of Elements* is an arrangement of the elements in horizontal rows according to their atomic numbers, which represent the number of protons in each atom. Each vertical column in the periodic table makes up a related group of elements.

Chemical bonds

Chemical bonds are forces that hold atoms together. These forces arise from the interaction of valence electrons. The two main types of chemical bonds are ionic and covalent. Consider two common substances, water (H_2O) and table salt or sodium chloride (NaCl).

In an ionic bond, valence electrons are transferred from one atom to one or more other atoms. The ionic bond between sodium (Na) and chlorine (Cl) is easily broken simply by applying a low voltage. The atom that loses electrons becomes a positive ion, while the atom that gains electrons becomes a negative ion. With NaCl, the resulting ions are sodium (Na+) and chlorine (Cl-). Ions in a solution can conduct a current.

By contrast, the bonds between hydrogen (H) and oxygen (O) in a water molecule are not easily broken. The bonds are covalent, meaning that the atoms share electrons rather than "give" or "take" them.

Chemical reactions

A chemical reaction is a process in which there is a chemical change, a fundamental alteration of the substance through the combination or separation of atoms or groups of atoms. During a chemical reaction, chemical bonds are broken and atoms are rearranged to form new bonds. A chemical reaction can be represented by an equation. For example, in the presence of oxygen (O), iron (Fe) undergoes a chemical change, and the result is rust. This can be represented symbolically:

$$Fe(s) + O_2 (g) \longrightarrow Fe_2O_3 (s)$$

$$Fe + O_2 \longrightarrow Fe_2O_3$$

In this equation, the reactants on the left are iron and oxygen. The product is rust. However, in close examination we notice that the equation is not balanced, meaning that there is not the same number of atoms of iron and oxygen on both sides of the equation. The conservation of mass is not demonstrated. Therefore, to more accurately represent what happens in this reaction, we must show that two molecules of iron and three molecules of oxygen react to produce two molecules of rust.

$$2Fe + 3O_2 \longrightarrow 2Fe_2O_3$$

Electromagnetic waves

The electromagnetic spectrum is a continuous range of waves extending from radio waves to gamma waves. The waves are classified according to their frequencies. Electromagnetic waves as low as 0.01 hertz have been detected. In an electromagnetic spectrum there are different bands of wavelengths, as shown in the table below.

10^{-14}m	10^{-11}m	10^{-8}m	10^{-6}m	10^{-5}m	10^{-2}m to 10^4m
Gamma rays	X rays	Ultraviolet light	Visible light	Infrared rays	Radio waves

The human eye can only detect light having wavelengths between about 1/30,000 and 1/60,000 of an inch, which is why we call this range of wavelengths *visible light*. We perceive wavelengths in the visible light spectrum as a rainbow, from short-wavelength violet (about 400 nanometers; 1 nanometer=10^{-9}m) to long-wavelength red (about 700 nm).

All waves have the properties of *reflection, diffraction, and interference*. The direction of magnetic force in all electromagnetic waves is perpendicular to thee direction in which the wave is moving. Electromagnetic waves are used in many ways. Gamma rays are used to treat cancer and many skin diseases. Ultraviolet rays are used in fluorescent lighting. X-rays are used to locate and treat internal diseases. Infrared rays are used in special lamps to treat some skin problems and are emitted by electric heaters, heat lamps, and toasters.

Theory of relativity

In 1905, Einstein put forth a theory of special relativity, followed by his theory of general relativity in 1915. These are mathematical theories, and understanding them requires more knowledge of mathematics than can be expected of the typical 9-12 student. In this discussion, therefore, we will use words to illustrate applications of the theories.

The *theory of special relativity* deals with uniform motion, motion of *constant velocity*. This may be illustrated as follows. Suppose you are moving on a bus, which is traveling smoothly and at a constant velocity. On the bus you drop a ball. The ball will appear to fall straight down. As long as the bus is moving smoothly and with constant velocity, the motion of objects on the bus will be the same as if you were on the ground. However, if the bus abruptly slows down or speeds up, the situation may be changed-the ball may not fall straight down. To state this as a principle, *if two systems move uniformly relative to each other, then all laws of motion are the same in both systems*. The theory of special relativity is based on two postulates:

1. All laws of nature are the same in all uniformly moving reference frames.

2. The speed of light in free space has the same measured value for all observers, regardless of the motion of the source or the motion of the observer. The speed of light is a constant.

The *theory of general relativity* deals with time, space, mass, motion, and gravitation. Isaac Newton helped us to understand gravity by concluding that two bodies attract each other with a force depending on their masses and their distances from one another. According to Einstein, if from inside an accelerating elevator under the pull of gravity an observer drops an object, the object will seem to hang in space. This is because the floor of the accelerating machine, as seen from outside the machine, is falling just as fast as the object. Einstein stated that it makes to difference if an object is acted upon by a gravitational force or is in an accelerated from of reference. This is the principle of *equivalence*, an aspect of the theory of general relativity.

Interaction of energy and matter, $E=mc^2$

Another major contribution by Einstein is his work on mass-energy equivalence. Matter, even at rest, possesses energy, which is called *rest energy*. Einstein put forth the idea that when mass disappears, energy is released. The formula expressing the amount of energy released is $E=mc^2$, where E is energy, m is mass, and c^2 is the conversion factor between mass and energy.

Kinetic molecular theory

Since the 17th century, gases were pictured to consist of small particles separated by large distances. In our discussion of energy, we talk about *kinetic energy*, the energy of a moving object. By the 19th century, scientists were able to think of the behavior of gases in terms of mass and velocity of the particles. At a given velocity, an object of greater mass has a greater energy.

Gases that behave as the kinetic molecular theory predicts are referred to as *ideal gases*. *ChemCom* (American Chemical Society, 1988) provides an overview of the kinetic molecular theory by presenting a set of postulates.

1. Gases consist of atoms or molecules that have negligible size compared to the distances separating them.

2. Gas molecules are in constant, random motion. Their collision with each other and the walls of a container results in gas pressure.

3. Even thought individual atoms or molecules may lose or gain energy, there is no net loss or gain of energy.

4. At a given temperature, molecules in a gas sample have a range of kinetic energy. However, the average energy of molecules is constant and depends only on the temperature of the sample. As the temperature increases, so does the average kinetic energy of the molecules.

Entropy and disorder

Whenever a physical system is free to distribute its energy, it does so in a manner that increases the level of disorder (entropy) in the system; thus, while the energy of the system decreases, the entropy increases. This interaction is expressed in the second law of thermodynamics, which states that heat never spontaneously flows from a cold object to a hot one. All systems tend to become more and more disordered as time progresses. As with keeping house, maintaining or restoring order to a system-if it is possible-requires putting energy *into* the system. The second law describes the most probable events, not only the possible ones.

An example is to compare a diamond to a helium-filled container. In the diamond, the chemical bonds of the atoms lock them into a rigid, orderly framework. We therefore can say that a diamond has low entropy. By contrast, the helium atoms move about in a haphazard manner, and the system has a high level of entropy.

Quantum theory

Many scientists have contributed to the work of freeing electrons from substances. One such approach is known as the *photoelectric effect*. This effect occurs when light shines on certain metal surfaces, causing electrons to be ejected from the surface. Ejection of electrons depends only on the frequency of light-the higher the frequency of light used, the greater the energy of the electrons ejected.

Scientists were not able to explain the photoelectric effect by the wave property of light, since the wave aspect of light cannot be concentrated to eject a single electron. Einstein put forth the idea that this could be explained by viewing light as a bundle of particles, called photons. The photons bombarded the metals, causing them to eject electrons. When targeting the material, the particle (in this case a photon) carries an energy proportional to its frequency.

This understanding of the photoelectric effect played on important role in the development of one of the most important ideas in physics, the *quantum theory*. Plank was a pioneer who theorized that radiation from a solid body could be possible only if the energy is not in a continuous form, as in the case of waves. However, it could be calculated if the energy is given off in discrete packets or bundles called quanta. The energy emitted by each quantum is proportional to the frequency of radiation of light. The explanation for this phenomenon is the dual aspect of matter-just as we can view light as having both a wave and particle property, we can view the electron as having both wave and particle aspects. A beam of electrons passing through slits exhibits the same type of diffraction pattern as light. This understanding led to a new field of study called *quantum mechanics*.

The photoelectric effect has many practical applications, including in smoke detectors, sorting mechanisms, automatic door openers, cameras, and alarm systems. A typical photocell has an inner coating of a metal such as potassium. When light of a suitable frequency falls on the coating, electrons are ejected from the metal and can be attracted to the positive terminal of the system, causing a current in the outside circuit.

C. STUDENTS' MISCONCEPTIONS

Many researchers have worked on identifying students' misconceptions and confusion related to the topics in this chapter. A synthesis of the work of some of these researchers is presented here. For specific titles and dates of their work, please consult the References section for the following researchers: Treagust; Krajcik; Whitely; Mashhadi; Borman; Novick, and Nussbaum; Nakhleh; Doran; Singh and Haass; Stepans, Beiswenger, and Dyche; Dyche, McClurg, Stepans, and Veath; Stepans and Veath.

- When asked to explain why water is liquid at room temperature and hydrogen sulfide (H_2S) is a gas at room temperature, many 12th graders responded correctly that intermolecular forces account for the difference. Most of the students, who were taking chemistry, knew a relationship exists between the strength of intermolecular forces and the melting/boiling point of a substance. However, only a small percentage of students could provide reasons. They believed intermolecular forces are the forces within a molecule. Also, many of these students had the idea that covalent bonds are broken when a substance changes state.

- Many students, after taking a year of chemistry, have factual information but do not develop a conceptual framework that helps them to understand other chemical phenomena and concepts. They can use the correct terms and apply formulas to get the right answers, but do not exhibit understanding of the concepts. Many chemistry students who are able to balance equations, are unable to give the molecular explanation for the reactions.

- Even more able students who have taken physics have difficulty assimilating the particle theory of matter. University students have unclear conceptions of wave-particle duality and quantum theory.

- Many students view electrons as moving along a straight line and think that electrons are distributed because of their collisions. The students' conception of the wave aspect of electrons is as a particle having mass and velocity, whose path of motion is along a wave.

- Students have a concrete picture of the atom, thinking of it in terms of their everyday experiences.

- Students' view instability of the atom as the result of a balance between an attractive electrical force and the motion of the electron. The thermodynamic problem of stability is not present in their views.

- Students believe that probabilistic treatment of wave-particle duality is really some kind of inaccuracy. They say that we talk in probabilistic terms because we just do not know where the electrons are.

- In a study of Australian, American, and Thai students, it was discovered that 33% of 11th graders and 23% of 12th graders correctly related electron sharing to covalent bonds, but had not considered the influence of electronegativity and the resulting unequal sharing of the electron pair on bond polarity. It also was found that 39% of the 11th graders and

25% of the 12th graders believed that repulsion between bonds determined molecular shape.

- In some studies, more than half the junior high school to university students maintained a primitive perception of solids, liquids, and gases as a continuous medium, rather than an aggregation of particles. Further, they do not internalize important aspects of the accepted particulate or atomic model of matter.

- Many secondary students believe such properties as electrical conductivity, color, and malleability are also properties of individual atoms.

- Many secondary students also believe that the molecules of the same substance change shape and have different weights in different phases. Many can name the parts of an atom, but cannot describe the interaction of atoms and nuclei.

- Interviews of high school students revealed a lack of understanding of acids and bases because they lacked fundamental understanding of the particulate model of matter and how that understanding relates to atoms, molecules, and ions. The research also found that students had difficulty moving from verbal descriptions to drawings, and that most of the students had difficulty understanding the role of ions in aqueous solutions.

- Even though college students showed slightly more understanding of density and buoyancy when compared with junior and senior high school students, the major distinction they demonstrated was the ability to use more sophisticated terminology, without the understanding.

- When interviewed about their ideas of the structure of atoms and molecules, many secondary students cited the structures of the models they had seen in books or the classroom. They described atoms and molecules as having spherical shapes and specific colors.

- Most of the junior high science students retain their views of the outward appearance of substances, i.e. shape, size, color, texture. Those who do change from this outward view still express naïve ideas. Instead of accepting ideas related to physical and chemical changes, the students take the scientific ideas in bits and pieces, mixed together with their preconceptions and ideas presented by books and other resources.

D. CONTRIBUTING FACTORS

Many researchers have shed some light on factors that contribute to students' science misconceptions. This section includes a synthesis of some of the work. Please refer to the References section for titles and dates of work incorporated here by the following authors: Rowe; Kesidou; Duit; Glynn; Wiser; Stepans and Veath; Stepans, Beiswenger, and Dyche.

- Rowe put chemistry on the "killer list," arguing that the short-term memory of our mental computer can manage only limited amounts of information at a time, contrary to the way chemistry is taught.

- Students are not challenged to explain the chemical processes behind the equations.

- Chemistry is presented as a mathematical exercise, equating numbers on one side to those on the other side.

- When new information is presented to students, several outcomes may occur. First, they may just accumulate the information without integrating it into their existing framework, adding new words without changing their explanations of a concept. Second, the information may not make sense within students' frameworks, so they may ignore it. Third, students may distort contradictory information to make it fit their existing framework, resulting in misconceptions.

- Guiding students from their everyday conceptions to accepted scientific conceptions is a difficult and lengthy process. Even providing experiences to encourage students to develop their frameworks may not be sufficient. Experiences may not help if they are not interpreted in the intended way.

- Most of the present textbooks and instructional methods do not take into account recent discoveries about how students learn. They also don't follow researchers' recommendations to find out what students bring into the learning environment and use that as a starting point for developing curriculum and instruction.

- Standardized tests of science achievement mainly assess factual recall but fail to detect the discrepancies between accepted scientific understanding and students' personal beliefs. Unfortunately, these tests play an important role in what is being taught and how.

- "Intuitive conceptions"–knowledge that is acquired from personal interaction with the environment–are difficult to dispel because they have been acquired over a lifetime and seem natural to the learner.

- Some concepts acquired from formal school instruction are in conflict with acceptable scientific meaning.

- Students' formation of ideas does not keep up with the increasingly abstract textbook explanation. Students often fill in ("invent") their own interpretations, resulting in confusion and misconceptions.

- The models we use to help concrete thinkers understand a concept may, in fact, create misconceptions. Sometimes our models are two-dimensional diagrams with symbols. Also, we often use ordinary materials to make physical models to represent things the students are unable to observe directly, such as using marshmallows and toothpicks to demonstrate molecules. Since most students are concrete thinkers, they adopt the models to represent the concept. For example, they believe that the bonds between atoms literally break in the way a toothpick would when pressure is applied. Furthermore, they may believe that when ice is heated its atoms actually expand, because that is what happens when marshmallows are heated.

- Overemphasis on terminology by teachers and textbooks is another factor contributing to students' confusion. Students learn that recognizing or memorizing the vocabulary is more important than understanding the concepts behind the terminology.

ACTIVITY 1. Elements

1. Commit

Place the following elements into categories. Explain the reasons for your classification.
H, Na, Mg, C, Al, Ca, N, O, Cl, He, Ar

2. Expose beliefs

Share your classification system and your rationale for it with others in your group. Ask someone to present the group's ideas to the rest of the class.

3. Confront views

Negotiate with others, using books, charts, and other resources about how to categorize the materials. Develop a set of criteria.

4. Accommodate the concept

Check your ideas by consulting the Periodic Table of Elements and other relevant materials. As you try to accommodate what you have learned from all of these resources, negotiate with others an understanding of how elements are grouped. What is the evidence provided by scientists to support what they know about the arrangement of elements in the periodic table?

5. Extend the concept

What are some examples, applications, and uses of what is known about the elements?

6. Go beyond

What other questions and problems do you have about properties of these or other elements? What steps will you take to pursue your questions and problems?

ACTIVITY 2: Chemical reactions

1. Commit

Write down your explanations of the following phenomena: lighting of a match, rust forming on iron, foaming of vinegar and baking soda mixture. In each case write statements, use symbols, or draw pictures to explain the causes.

2. Expose beliefs

Share your ideas and explanations with others in your group. Ask someone to present the group's ideas to the rest of the class. Pay attention to the views of others. Question and challenge the views that are presented.

3. Confront views

Confront and test the ideas that have been presented by observing a demonstration by your teacher or consulting appropriate written or electronic resources. Then negotiate with others to decide about the scientific explanations for these occurrences. What is your new understanding of these phenomena?

4. Accommodate the concept

What are some examples of chemical reactions with which you are familiar? Write them symbolically and check with your instructor, classmates, and other resources.

5. Extend the concept

What are some examples of slow and fast reactions? Investigate the meanings and find examples of such phenomena as oxidation, reduction, combustion, endothermic reactions, and exothermic reactions.

6. Go beyond

What other questions and problems can you think of related to chemical reactions, including questions that are possible to pursue and those that are not, and the reasons behind them?

ACTIVITY 3: Structure of the atom

1. Commit

Describe the structure of the hydrogen atom, or draw it, labeling all parts. In your description, pay attention to the nature, characteristics, and role of all of the parts that make up the atom.

2. Expose beliefs

Share your drawings and your descriptions with others in your group. Negotiate with others about everyone's drawings and explanations. Ask someone to present your group's final drawing to the rest of the class.

3. Confront views

Consult books and other resources. Compare your drawings with those in these resources. To what extent do your ideas agree with the explanations given by scientists, such as Neils Bohr? How have the ideas and mental models about of scientists changed in light of ongoing investigation and evidence?

4. Accommodate the concept

As you are trying to resolve conflicts between what you thought and what the experts say, pay attention to their evidence. How do they support what they say? How have the ideas and mental models evolved in the past 80 years or so?

5. Extend the concept

What are some questions and problems you want to pursue related to the structure of the atom? You may consider questions about the atoms that make up other elements.

ACTIVITY 4: Nuclear Fission and fusion

1. Commit

You may be familiar with the terms "fission" and "fusion." Write down what these terms mean to you. How did you hear and learn about these concepts?

2. Expose beliefs

Share your views with others in your small group. Ask someone to present the views of your group to others in class.

3. Confront views

In your small group, consult appropriate instructional materials to compare your views with those in these resources. Negotiate in your group to come up with clear definitions for fission and fusion.

4. Accommodate the concept

Secure appropriate written materials demonstrating what experts say about how they know that these phenomena occur and what evidence they have to support their ideas.

5. Extend the concept

Cite applications of fission and fusion with which you are familiar. If you cannot think of any applications, ask your teacher for examples.

6. Go beyond

Write down additional questions and problems you could pursue about fission and fusion.

ACTIVITY 5: Quantum theory

1. Commit

Based on what you have read or heard, what can you say about the quantum theory? Write down your ideas, make drawings, and/or use symbols to express what you know.

2. Expose beliefs

Share your ideas with others in your group. Have someone from your group present all of the ideas from your group to the rest of the class.

3. Confront views

Find resource materials describing quantum theory and check your ideas with those presented in the resources. As a group, negotiate about the meaning of the quantum theory.

4. Accommodate the concept

Consult books and other resources to find evidence presented by scientists about the underlying thoughts behind the quantum theory and the reasons for their thinking.

5. Extend the concept

What are some applications of this theory? What speculated applications of quantum theory have become incorporated into popular science fiction writing and films?

6. Go beyond

What are additional questions and problems you could pursue about quantum theory? Present plans that you would follow to answer your questions and problems.

ACTIVITY 6: Theory of relativity

1. Commit

Suppose you are on a smoothly running train that is moving at a constant velocity. Inside the train you drop a ball. What do you think will be the direction of its fall? Draw a picture describing the path it will follow and explain your reasoning. What would happen to the ball if you did the same thing while you were standing outside the train?

2. Expose beliefs

Share your views and ideas with others in your group. Use words, drawings, and symbols. Have someone from your group present all of the ideas from your group to the rest of the class.

3. Confront views

Confront your ideas and those of others by observing a demonstration or consulting written resources. Examine resources to find what evidence and reasoning scientists use to support the theory.

4. Accommodate the concept

In your group, use class ideas, the demonstrations, and the evidence provided by scientists to negotiate an explanation for the theory of special relativity.

5. Extend the concept

Write down applications and examples of where the special relativity theory is evident.

6. Go beyond

We have been discussing issues related to what is known as *special* relativity. What is the theory of *general* relativity and what are some examples and problems that may be addressed by it?

What are some questions or problems you would like to pursue related to either the special or general theories of relativity?

ACTIVITY 7: E=mc²

1. Commit

You probably have seen this equation before. Individually, write down what relationship the equation means to you. What do the symbols represent? Where did you learn about this relationship?

2. Expose beliefs

Share your views with others in your group. You do not have to necessarily agree with everyone in the group. Write down everybody's ideas on a large sheet of paper, then ask someone from the group to present the ideas to the entire class.

3. Confront views

In your small group, consult books, journals, the Internet, and other resources to check your views against the claims and evidence presented by scientists and other experts.

4. Accommodate the concept

Keep track of the new insights you have developed as a result of your investigations. Negotiate a new understanding with others in your group.

5. Extend the concept

Examine written and other resources and consult your instructor for examples and applications of mass-energy equivalence as expressed in this equation.

6. Go beyond

Decide on a set of questions and problems that you would like to pursue related to $E=mc^2$.

ACTIVITY 8: Chemical bonds

1. Commit

We all have seen such symbolic representations as NaCl (sodium chloride, table salt) and H_2O (water). NaCl consists of a sodium atom and a chlorine atom combined, and H_2O consists of two hydrogen atoms and one oxygen atom. Using picture, statements, and symbols, express your views on how these substances are similar and different with respect to the forces that hold their atoms together.

2. Expose beliefs

Share your ideas with others in your group. Every member of the group should share their statements, drawings, and symbolic representations. Ask someone from the group to present all of the group's ideas to the rest of the class.

3. Confront views

Using written materials, compare your views about the forces holding the salt and water atoms together with the views of scientists.

4. Accommodate the concept

In your group, identify the evidence the scientists use to support their views. Weigh the strengths and weaknesses of various views that you find, then negotiate an explanation for the chemical bonding between the atoms in salt and water.

5. Extend the concept

Search for or give your own examples and applications of various chemical bonds. What are the uses of different kinds of chemical bonding in our lives and in the world around us?

6. Go beyond

What are some other questions and problems related to chemical bonds that you would like to pursue? What steps will you take to pursue these questions and problems?

ACTIVITY 9: Electromagnetic waves

1. Commit

Scientists tell us that there is a limit to what the eye can see. Write down your ideas about what the human eye can or cannot see. Write down reasons for what you think. Where did you get your ideas?

2. Expose beliefs

In your small group, share your views, drawing on personal experiences and knowledge. Pay attention tot he views presented by others in your group. Question and challenge the ideas presented while keeping an open mind. Volunteer someone to present the group's ideas to the rest of the class.

3. Confront views

Consult written materials, your teacher, and other resources about what the human eye is capable of seeing, then compare what you find with the views presented by the members of the class.

4. Accommodate the concept

Negotiate with others in your group to develop a sense of what is meant by the *spectrum of electromagnetic waves*. Draw pictures, identifying the regions of ultraviolet, infrared, X- , and gamma rays, visible light, and other kinds of electromagnetic radiation. Discuss the special characteristics of each band of radiation.

5. Extend the concept

With the aid of the teacher and other resources, discuss in your group the effects and applications of different bands of radiation.

6. Go beyond

What are some questions and problems that you would like to pursue about electromagnetic waves? How will you pursue your questions and problems?

ACTIVITY 10: Kinetic molecular theory

1. Commit

Individually express your views about the properties and behavior of gas molecules, using words, drawings, and models.

2. Expose beliefs

Share your views with others in your group and record everyone's ideas. Then ask a member of your group to share these ideas with the rest of the class. Challenge and question all of the ideas that are presented by the class.

3. Confront views

Use classroom resources, your teacher's explanations, and demonstrations to learn about the evidence presented by scientists to support their views about how molecules behave.

4. Accommodate the concept

As you consider the ideas and evidence presented, develop an explanation about kinetic molecular theory that makes sense to you.

5. Extend the concept

Write down some applications of this theory. What are some examples of the properties of gases with which you are familiar?

6. Go beyond

What are some questions and problems you could pursue? What steps would you take to pursue them?

ACTIVITY 11: Entropy

1. Commit

What if you are given a piece of diamond and a balloon filled with helium gas. If you had access to an instrument that enabled you to see the atoms in the diamond and inside the balloon, what would they look like? Concentrate on the degree of order or disorder of the atoms. Express your views by writing down a statement, drawing a picture, or building a model. Give reasons for your ideas.

2. Expose beliefs

Share your views with others in your group. Have a group member present everyone's ideas to the rest of the class.

3. Confront views

Confront your ideas by checking written and other resources. Within your group, negotiate an understanding about the relationship of the order or disorder among the atoms to the nature of the diamond and helium.

4. Accommodate the concept

Continue to consult resources in your group to develop an explanation of the concept of *entropy*. What is the relationship between energy and entropy?

5. Extend the concept

What are some applications of the concept of entropy? What are the *laws of thermodynamics and how are they related to entropy?*

6. Go beyond

What are some questions or problems you would pursue about entropy and how would you conduct this study?

References

American Chemical Society. (1988). *ChemCom–Chemistry in the Community.* Dubuque, IA: Kendall-Hunt.

Bilash, B. (1997). *A demo a day: A year of physical science demonstrations.* Batavia, IL: Flinn Scientific, Inc.

Borghi, L., DeAmbrosis, A., and Ghisolfi, E. (1993). Teaching special relativity in high school. *Proceedings, Third International Conference on Students' Mathematics and Science Misconceptions.* Ithaca, NY: Cornell University Press.

Bormann, M. (1987). Students' alternative framework in the field of particle and wave models of light and electrons. In W. Kuhn (Ed.), Didactic der physik, voltage, physikertagung. Berlin: Gieben.

Doran, Rodney L., Lawrenz, Frances, and Helgeson, Stanley. (1994). Research on assessment in science. In D. Gable, Ed., *Handbook of research in science teaching and learning.* NY: Macmillan Publishing.

Dyche, S., McClurg, P., Stepans, J., and Veath, L. (1993). Questions and conjectures concerning models, misconceptions, and spatial ability. *School Science and Mathematics* 93(4), April, pp. 191-197.

Freeman, Ira. (1965). *Physics Made Simple.* Garden City, NY: Made Simple Books.

Gable, Dorothy L. (Ed.) (1994). *Handbook of research in science teaching and learning.* NY: Macmillan Publishing.

Glynn, S. M. and Duit, R. (Eds.). (1995). *Learning science in the schools.* Mahwah, NJ: Erlbaum Publishing.

Glynn, Shawn M., Yeany, Russel H., and Britton, Bruce K. (Eds.) (1991). The psychology of learning science. Mahwah, NJ: Erlbaum Publishing.

Hess, Fred C. Revised by Arthur Thomas. (1953). *Chemistry Made Simple.* Garden City, NY: Made Simple Books, Doubleday and Co., Inc.

Hewitt, Paul G., Suchocki, John, and Hewitt, Leslie, A. (1999). *Conceptual physical science, 2nd ed.* Menlo Park, CA: Addison-Wesley Publishers.

Kesidou, S., Duit, R., and Glynn S. (1995). Conceptual development in physics: students' understanding of heat. In Glynn, S, & R. Duit (Eds.). *Learning science in the schools.* Mahwah, NJ: Erlbaum.

Krajcik, Joseph. (1991). Developing students' understanding of chemical concepts. In Glynn, S, & R. Duit (Eds.). *Learning science in the schools.* Mahwah, NJ: Erlbaum.

Lewicki, Daniel. (1993). The effects of a constructivist method of instruction in a general chemistry laboratory on college students' achievement and conceptual change. *Proceedings, Third International Conference on Students' Mathematics and Science Misconceptions.* Ithaca, NY: Cornell University Press.

Mashhadi, Azam. (1993). What is the nature of the understanding of the concept of "wave-particle duality" among pre-university physics students? *Proceedings, Third International Conference on Students' Mathematics and Science Misconceptions.* Ithaca, NY: Cornell University Press.

Nakhleh, M. B. (1992). Why some students don't learn chemistry. *The Journal of Chemical Education.* 69(3): 292-296.

Nakhleh, Mary B. (1993). Students' models of matter in the context of acid-base chemistry. *Proceedings, Third International Conference on Students' Mathematics and Science Misconceptions.* Ithaca, NY: Cornell University Press.

National Research Council. (1996). *National Science Education Standards.* Washington, DC: National Academy Press.

Rowe, Mary Budd. (1983). Getting chemistry off the killer course list. *Journal of Chemical Education* 60(11):954-956.

Singh, Sukhwindar and Haas, Mary. (1993). Empowering the learning of chemistry through curriculum development: implications of misconceptions research for NSTA's project on Scope, Sequence, and Coordination of Secondary School Science, Grades 6-12. *Proceedings, Third International Conference on Students' Mathematics and Science Misconceptions.* Ithaca, NY: Cornell University Press.

Stepans, J. I. (1991). Developmental patterns in student's understanding of physics concepts. In Glynn, S, & R. Duit (Eds.). *The psychology of learning science.* Hillsdale, NJ: Erlbaum.

Stepans, J., Beiswenger, R., and Dyche, S. (1986). Misconceptions die hard. *The Science Teacher,* September, 1986, pp. 65-69.

Stepans, J. and Veath, L. (1990). Caution: the models you use to help concrete learners could also be creating misconceptions. *Science Scope,* Nov-Dec 1990, pp. 51-52.

Stepans, J. and Veath, L. (1994). How do students really explain changes in matter. *Science Scope,* May, 1994, pp. 31-35.

Treagust, David F. (1995). Diagnostic assessment of students' science knowledge. In Glynn, S, & R. Duit (Eds.). *Learning science in the schools.* Mahwah, NJ: Erlbaum.

Whitely, Peter. (1993). Caribbean high school students' conceptions of the kinetic model of Matter. *Proceedings, Third International Conference on Students' Mathematics and Science Misconceptions.* Ithaca, NY: Cornell University Press.

Wiser, M. (1986). *The differentiation of heat and temperature: an evaluation of the effects of microcomputer teaching on students' misconceptions. Technical report.* Cambridge, MA: Harvard Graduate School of Education.

GEOMETRY

The teaching for conceptual change strategy can be used in areas other than science. This set of activities demonstrates its use in mathematics.

A.   IDENTIFICATION OF THE CONCEPTS

perimeter, conservation of perimeter, area, relationship between area and perimeter, surface area of solids, relationship between surface area and volume.

B.   BACKGROUND INFORMATION FOR THE TEACHER

What is perimeter? What is conservation of perimeter? How does that affect area?

The *perimeter* is the distance around a shape. Perimeter is measured in linear units: inches, centimeters, miles, and so on. From a given length of string or fence, many shapes can be made, but all of those shapes will have the same perimeter (as long as no string or fence is left over). This is called *conservation of perimeter*.

The *area* is how much of a surface is covered, or enclosed within the perimeter. Area is measured in square units: square inches, square centimeters, square feet, etc. Given a specific length of string, we can enclose the largest area in the form of a circle. Less area will be enclosed in a square, and even less in a rectangle.

What if area is kept constant and we make 3-D shapes?

Given a certain amount of area (such as a sheet of paper), regardless of the shape into which it is converted the surface area (coverage) does not change. For example, if we roll it into a tube to make a cylinder, the *surface area* of the cylinder is the same whether we roll it lengthwise or width-wise (Figure I). On the other hand, the *volume* (amount of space enclosed by the cylinder) depends on which way we roll it. The tall cylinder has more height but a smaller diameter than the short cylinder; however, these differences in height and diameter do not offset one another.

Figure I

Are the volumes of the two cylinders different? How can it be shown? Let us illustrate this with some numbers.

If we cut a cylinder to one-half its height, its volume is cut by one-half. If, on the other hand, we reduce the diameter of a cylinder to one-half its original value and keep the height the same, the volume will be cut by one-fourth.

The volume of a cylinder is represented by the equation: volume = (area of base) x (height). Since the area of the base is calculated as πr^2, where **r** is the radius (1/2 the diameter), we get the following formula for determining the volume of a cylinder:
$V = (\pi r^2)H$, **(H is the height of the cylinder)**

The length of an ordinary sheet of paper is 28 centimeters.

Figure II a: If it is made into a cylinder lengthwise, the diameter is 7 centimeters (so the radius is 3.5 centimeters). The volume of the cylinder is calculated as follows:

$V = (\pi r^2)H$, with **r** = 3.5 cm, **H** = 28 cm, and, as usual, π = 3.14.
Therefore, the volume of this cylinder = 3.14 x $(3.5)^2$ x 28 = 1077 cm^3

Figure II a

Figure II b: If the height is cut in half, to **H** = 14 cm, then **V** = 3.14 x $(3.5)^2$ x 14 = 538.5 cm^3. Note that the volume is also cut in half in this case.

Figure II b

<u>Figure II c</u>: If the diameter is cut in half, and therefore the radius too, then **r** = 1.75 cm and we have **V** = 3.14 x (1.75)² x 28 = 269.25 cm³. Note that here the volume is *one-quarter* of what it was initially (Figure II a).

Figure II c

<u>Figure II d</u>: Finally, if we just roll a full-sized sheet of paper into a tube width-wise, so it is shorter but thicker, **H** = 21.5 cm, and **r** = 4.5 cm. In this case, **V** = 3.14 x (4.5)² x 21.5 = 1367 cm³. Note that the volume of the cylinder is larger than when the paper was rolled length-wise.

Figure II d

C.   SOME REPRESENTATIVE STUDENT MISCONCEPTIONS ABOUT THESE CONCEPTS

◆   A change in the *shape* made from a constant length of string or fencing changes the *length*.

◆   Areas enclosed by the same length are the same.

◆   Volumes of shapes created by the same sheet of paper are equal.

◆   The surface areas of two different tubes made from a sheet of paper are different.

D. SOURCES OF STUDENTS' CONFUSION AND MISCONCEPTIONS

♦ Traditionally, geometry instruction goes through the sequence of: **point → line → plane → solid**. This sequence is <u>opposite</u> to the sequence in which learners learn, which is from a concrete form (solid) to the most abstract concept (point).

♦ Instruction emphasizes terms and formulas before the learner is ready.

♦ There is a mismatch between how a student develops and the assumptions the instructional materials make.

♦ Many geometric concepts are quite abstract and require a certain level of formal thinking and skill that many students may not have.

E. LEARNING ABOUT PERIMETER, AREA, AND VOLUME USING THE CONCEPTUAL CHANGE MODEL

TEACHING NOTES

Provide the following materials for each small group:

> several standard sheets of paper
> tape
> beans (or rice or popcorn kernels) for filler
> string
> flashlights
> rulers

It will be very helpful to have centimeter grid paper available for students to work on when "building fences" in Activity I. The grids will provide a method for determining area units without making calculations. Some students will want to use the grid paper for covering cylinders in Activity II in order to assure themselves that the surface area is the same for both cylinders.

ACTIVITY I: The Fence

1. Commit to an Outcome

Consider the following situation:

A farmer had a piece of fence. He used it to enclose part of a pasture, as shown in Figure 1a below:

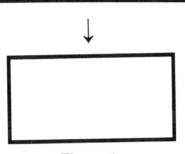

Figure 1 a

The following year, he took the same piece of fence and enclosed another part of the pasture, as in Figure 1 b:

Figure 1 b

During the third year, he enclosed another part of the field, as in Figure 1 c:

Figure 1 c

He was puzzled and asked himself these questions comparing the three situations:

  a.   Do I have more distance to walk around?
  b.   Do I have less distance to walk around ?
  c.   Do I have the same distance to walk around?

The farmer also wondered, given similar conditions for all three pieces:

  d.   Do my cows have more grass to eat?
  e.   Do my cows have less grass to eat?
  f.   Do my cows have the same amount of grass to eat?

Write down your predictions.

2. Expose Beliefs

Share your predictions and explanations in your small group. Based on your sharing with others in your group, do you want to make any changes in your ideas? Select a representative to present the predictions and the explanations of each member to the rest of the class.

3. Confront Beliefs

Get the necessary materials and test your predictions. What did you observe? Did your observations agree with your predictions? Any surprises? Do you want to make any changes in your thinking?

4. Accommodate the Concept

Based on what you have observed and the discussions in your group, what statement can you make about what happens to <u>length</u> and <u>area</u> when shape changes? Share your thoughts and statements with others.

5. Extend the Concept

If, from a given length, you made the shapes of a rectangle, square, and circle, how would the areas compare? What are some of the applications of this concept?

6. Go Beyond

Think of additional questions, problems, or projects you want to pursue related to the geometric concepts covered here.

ACTIVITY II. Covering Cylinders

1. Commit to an Outcome

Consider the following situation:
We have an ordinary sheet of paper.
We can construct a cylinder (a) length-wise or (b) width-wise, as shown.

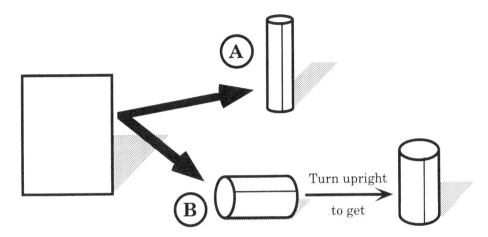

Make predictions as to which of the following will be true :

    a.   It takes the same amount of material to COVER the outside of each cylinder.
    b.   It takes more material to COVER (a).
    c.   It takes more material to COVER (b).

Give reasons for your prediction.

2. Expose Beliefs

Share your predictions and explanations with others in your group.

3. Confront Beliefs

Get sheets of paper and some tape, construct the cylinders, and design a way to test your predictions. (Save your cylinders for the next activity.)

4. Accommodate the concept based on what you have observed and the discussions in your group, what statement can you make about the amount of coverage of cylinders - one length-wise, and one width size?

5. What are some applications of this?

6. Think of additional questions, problems, or projects that you can pursue.

ACTIVITY III. Filling the cylinders

1. Commit to Outcome

For the cylinders you have constructed, predict which of the following will be true.

  a. It takes the same amount of beans to FILL cylinders (A) and (B).
  b. It takes more beans to FILL cylinder (A).
  c. It takes more beans to FILL cylinder (B).

Give reasons for your prediction.

2. Expose Beliefs

Share with others in your group your predictions and explanations on filling the cylinders constructed from same-sized sheets of paper. Have someone from your group present your predictions and explanations to the rest of the class. Be sure your group's explanations and predictions are recorded on the class chart.

3. Confront Beliefs

In your group, construct ways to test your predictions and explanations, using any materials you need. Based on your observations, work toward resolving any conflict between your predictions and explanations and what you observed.

4. Accommodate the Concept

Based on your observations and discussion, try to contruct your own meaning about surface area and volume. In changing shapes (going from cylinder a to cylinder b, & cylinder c), what happened to the surface area? What happened to the volume as we went from cylinder a to cylinder b, & cylinder c? What statement can you make about these situations?

5. Extend the Concept

What are some other examples related to surface area and volume, as they appeared here? What are some of the applications of the relationship between area and volume?

6. Go Beyond

Identify other questions and problems related to surface area and volume that you like to pursue and bring those ideas to share with the rest of the class.

ACTIVITY IV: Shapes of the Shadows

1. Commit to an Outcome

For the cylinders you constructed in Activity III, consider the following questions. If you cast shadows of the surface of the cylinders, what would be the shape of the shadows? How would the sizes of the shadows compare? Give reasons for your predictions. (Make sure the distance of the light source, the object, and the screen are the same for both situations.)

2. Expose Beliefs

Share the reasons for your explanations and predictions with your small group.

3. Confront Beliefs

Get the cylinders, cast the shadows, and test your predictions about the shapes and sizes of the shadows cast by the cylinders.

4. Accommodate the Concept

Based on your observations and discussions, what statement can you make about the geometry of shadows? Share your statements with others.

5. Extend the Concept

What are the applications of what you have seen here? From the teacher, get different geometric solids and challenge others in your group or in other groups to predict the shadows of the solids. Also, your teacher may show you shadows of hidden objects. Can you identify the shapes that are casting the shadows?

6. Go Beyond

Think of additional projects, questions, and problems you would like to pursue related to the geometry of shadows. Bring your ideas to class to share.

ACTIVITY V. Filling cylinders made of cut paper

1. Commit to an outcome

You can make a cylinder with a regular sheet of paper (a). You also can cut the paper in half and tape the ends together to construct a cylinder (b). You also can cut the paper into thirds to construct a cylinder (c). If you were to fill all three cylinders with something like sand or popcorn, which of the following do you think would result?

   a. All three cylinders will hold the same amount of material.
   b. The cylinder made of the paper cut in half will hold the most.
   c. The cylinder made of the paper cut in thirds will hold the most.
   d. The cylinder made of the whole paper will hold the most.

2. Expose beliefs

Share your predictions and explanation with others in your group. Then ask someone in your group to share everyone's predictions and explanations with the whole group.

3. Confront views

Gather the necessary materials and test your ideas. How did your observations compare with your predictions? Based on what you observed, what changes would you like to make in your explanations?

4. Accommodate observations and explanations

Based on what you have observed and heard, what explanation would you provide for what you have observed?

5. Extend the concept

What are some examples and applications of what you have observed?

6. Go beyond

What are some new questions or problems would you like to pursue related to this activity? What steps will you take to pursue your questions?

F. REFERENCES

Hart, K. (May, 1984). Which comes first—length, area, or volume? *The Arithmetic Teacher*, *16-18*, 26-27.

Hildreth, D. (January 1983). The use of strategies in estimating measurements. *The Arithmetic Teacher*, 50-54.

Leyden, M. (October 1985). The strange silos. *Science and Children*, 32-33.

Zaslavsky, C. (September 1989). People who live in round houses. *The Arithmetic Teacher*, 18-21.

PLANNING FOR ADDITIONAL TOPICS

Now that you are familiar with the Conceptual Change Model, you may want to plan activities for additional topics using the model. The next five pages may be used as a template for such planning.

The first page provides space for Identification of the Concept and listing of Background Information. (This might include notes about background resources you are already using and a list of your expectations of students. See page 10 for a sample list.)

The second page provides space for listing Representative Students' Misconceptions and Sources of Student Confusion and Misconceptions. (Make notes about these based on your interactions with students, information you read in professional journals, and discussions with other teachers regarding their experiences with students.)

Use the third page to make a list of materials necessary for the student activities, safety tips, and advance preparation requirements.

The fourth page lists the stages of the Conceptual Change Model. Make a copy of this page for each activity that you plan. Sometimes you will plan all six stages for an activity. Other times you will use stages 1-3 or 1-4 for individual activities, then plan stages 4-6 after a series of related activities. Give some thought to the questions yu may ask students during each stage.

The fifth page is for assessment. As you think about your expectations of students for the concept you have chosen, write down ideas and rubrics you may use to assess the degree to which the student have met those expectations. (Pages 11–14 contain brief discussion and sample rubrics.)

A.   IDENTIFICATION OF THE CONCEPTS

B.   SUMMARY OF KEY POINTS TO BE ADDRESSED

C.   EXPECTATIONS OF STUDENTS

D.   SOME REPRESENTATIVE STUDENT MISCONCEPTIONS

E.   SOURCES OF STUDENTS' CONFUSION AND MISCONCEPTIONS

F.   LEARNING ABOUT _____ USING THE
CONCEPTUAL CHANGE MODEL

TEACHING NOTES

Materials for Activities:

Advance Preparation Notes:

Safety Reminders:

ACTIVITY

1. **Commit to an Outcome**

2. **Expose Beliefs**

3. **Confront Beliefs**

4. **Accommodate the Concept**

5. **Extend the Concept**

6. **Go Beyond**

G.   APPROPRIATE ASSESSMENTS

Author Joseph Stepans, professor of science and mathematics education at the University of Wyoming, has a B.S. in physics, a master's degree in physics, and a Ph.D. in science education. Dr. Stepans has been active in misconceptions research since 1981, and has been published extensively. In addition, he has shared his work in hundreds of presentations at state, regional, national, and international conferences.